BANANAS

BANANAS

EDITED BY EMMA TENNANT
ART EDITOR: JULIAN ROTHENSTEIN

Quartet

LONDON, MELBOURNE, NEW YORK
IN ASSOCIATION WITH BLOND & BRIGGS

PUBLISHED BY QUARTET BOOKS LIMITED, 1977
A MEMBER OF THE NAMARA GROUP
27 GOODGE STREET, LONDON W1P 1FD

IN ASSOCIATION WITH BLOND & BRIGGS LIMITED

COPYRIGHT © 1977 BY *BANANAS* AND INDIVIDUAL
CONTRIBUTORS
INTRODUCTION COPYRIGHT © 1977 BY
EMMA TENNANT
ILLUSTRATIONS COPYRIGHT © 1977 BY *BANANAS*
AND INDIVIDUAL ARTISTS AND PHOTOGRAPHERS

BOOK DESIGN: JULIAN ROTHENSTEIN
FRONTISPIECE: HIANG KEE

ISBN 0 7043 3176 4

PRINTED BY UNWIN BROTHERS LIMITED
THE GRESHAM PRESS, OLD WOKING, SURREY

for Colin

INTRODUCTION

Bananas began in January 1975 with a specific aim. This was to introduce to as many readers as possible a selection of lively new writing by known and unknown writers, and to prove, in a country where 'little magazines' are virtually unread and undistributed, that people do take an interest in fiction of a high standard if they can get hold of it. The appearance and attitude of most of the magazines of writing and criticism seemed dreary and academic, despite the often excellent contents, and it was for this reason that we chose to make *Bananas* a newspaper: you could read stories as if they were the latest reports from the writer's brain rather than 'timeless' literature, and have the space for big, arresting illustrations and original drawings as well. We decided to have the occasional major piece of criticism – Tom Nairn and Martin Seymour-Smith's analyses of the English literary intelligentsia and the state of writing today in England are both included here – but to eschew reviews. Too often the reviews take over and short stories are thrown out, or a couple remain, uneasily sandwiched between interviews and criticism, in literary magazines of this kind. We would print stories up to 7,000 words in length, and give poems plenty of room. In each issue there would be a 'supplement', with a specific theme, and writers would be asked to write stories, or jokes, or riddles round this theme; and it was interesting to see how well this worked. Many of the stories, of course, were uncommissioned, and yet it was odd to note that, with each issue, a theme emerged. There was some annoyance with the first number, where (innocently) we printed stories which seemed to deal mainly with the killing of men ·by women, and a lack of annoyance when, a few issues later, much of the fiction concerned the killing of women by men – so well accepted a subject, I suppose, that there can be no

8

grounds for complaint. In our Fac' supplement, from which John Sladek's brilliant *After Flaubert* is printed here, a collection of writers examined the received ideas of the age. Claud Cockburn and Miles (founder of IT and Burroughs's bibliographer) gave, in their 'literary memoirs', fresh and witty accounts of their meetings with famous writers – and in this volume we can see Cockburn's view of Ezra Pound, Miles's time with Ginsberg. But most of all, of course, there was the excitement of finding a really good story, and knowing it could be bought at a railway bookstall and read on the way home in the train.

Gloomy prophecies that a magazine of this type could only find a very limited readership proved false. Once *Bananas* was made available in newsagents and bookshops all over the country, people started to buy it. Subscriptions went up, from people and libraries. Manuscripts came in in large numbers. The magazine began to be attacked in critical quarterlies, always a good sign, and Auberon Waugh called it pretentious rubbish. Meanwhile people went on writing stories and more people went on reading them.

Of the new, young and less well known writers included here, Martin Ryle, Sara Maitland and Tim Owens have all produced original and talented work, while J. G. Ballard's *The Dead Time* and Angela Carter's *The Company of Wolves* are, in my view, some of the best writing they have ever done. Hilary Bailey's caustic eye, in her story *Middle Class Marriage Saved*, is at its sharpest; Ruth Fainlight's *Dr Clock's Last Case* is extremely alarming, and subtly and cleverly done: funny too. Alan Sillitoe and Beryl Bainbridge deal with irritation brilliantly; Peter Wollen, in *Friendship's Death*, shows us a robot dealing with the world and finally, in an extraordinary burst of creative energy, making his own translation of Mallarmé.

Then there are the poems. One of the most startling is by Daniel Brand, who was seventeen at the time of writing (he is nineteen now). The poets we chose for this collection are all regular contributors and all, with the exception of Marilyn Hacker, English. There is a lot of scope and vigour in their poetry.

There's plenty of flavour in *Bananas*, and we hope you enjoy the read.

EMMA TENNANT June 1977

9

Angela Carter
The Company of Wolves

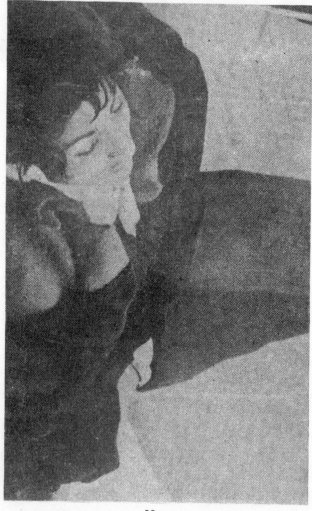

ONE BEAST, and only one, howls in the woods by night. The wolf is carnivore incarnate and he's as cunning as he is ferocious; once he's had a taste of human flesh, then nothing else will do. At night, the eyes of wolves shine like little candle-flames, yellowish, reddish, but that is because the pupils of their eyes grow fat, at night, and catch the light from your lantern to flash it back to you – red for danger; if a wolf's eyes reflect only the moonlight, then they gleam a cold and unnatural green, a mineral, a piercing colour, and if the benighted traveller spies those luminous, green, terrible sequins stiched suddenly upon the black thickets, then he knows he must run quick as he can, if fear has not struck him stock still, or the savage beast will rip out his throat.

But those eyes are all you will be able to glimpse of the forest assassins as they cluster invisibly around your smell of meat as you go through the wood unwisely late. They will be like shadows, they will be like wraiths, grey members of a congregation of nightmare; hark! his long, wavering howl . . . even by this snug fireside, with the door well barred, the loaded rifle hanging over the chimney breast, we shiver, though not with cold, when the wind blows their keenings to us on the cold air. The hair rises on the back of our necks. Their arias are fear made audible. Wolfsong is the sound of the rending you will suffer, in itself a murdering.

It is winter and cold weather. In this region of mountain and forest, there is nothing, now, for the wolves to eat, goats and sheep are in the byre, the deer have fled to the remaining pasturage of the southern slopes, the wolves grow lean and famished. There is so little flesh on them that you could count the starveling ribs through their pelts, if they gave you time before they pounced. Those slavering jaws; the lolling tongue; the rime of saliva on the grizzled chops – of all the teeming perils of the night and the forest, ghosts, hobgoblins, ogres that grill babies upon gridirons, witches that fatten their captives in cages for cannibal tables, the wolf is worst for he cannot listen to reason, his prick ears will not hear your pleas.

Fear and flee the wolf, little one, for, worst of all, a wolf may be more than he seems.

You are always in danger in the forest, where no people are. Step between the portals of the great pines where the shaggy branches tangle about you, trapping the unwary traveller in nets as if the vegetation itself were in a plot with the wolves who live there, as though the wicked trees go fishing on behalf of their friends – step between the gateposts of the inimical forest with the greatest trepidation and infinite precautions, my precious, for if you stray from the path for one instant, the wolves will eat you. They are grey as famine, as unkind as plague.

The grave-eyed children of the sparse villages always carry knives with them when they go out to tend the little flocks of goats that provide the homesteads with acrid milk and rank, maggotty cheeses. Their knives are half as big as they are and the blades are sharpened daily, like their wits. So they defend their goats against the wolves, and themselves, too.

But the wolves have ways of arriving at your own hearth-side. We try and try, but sometimes we cannot keep them out. Many's the winter's night the cottager sees a lean, grey, famished snout questing under the door and there was a woman once bitten in her own kitchen, as she was straining the macaroni. And, furthermore, lycanthropia's a bane, hereabouts.

Not so very long ago, a young woman in our village married a man who vanished clean away on her wedding night. The bed was made with new sheets and the bride lay down in it; the groom said, he was going out to relieve himself, insisted on it, for the sake of decency, and she drew the coverlet up to her chin and she lay there. And she waited and she waited and then she waited again – surely he's been gone a long time? Until she jumps up in bed, and shrieks to hear a howling, coming on the wind from the forest.

That long-drawn-out, wavering howl has, for all its fearful resonances, some inherent sadness in it, as if the beasts would love to be less beastly if only they knew how and, in some sense, mourn their own condition. There is a vast melancholy in the canticles of the wolves, melancholy infinite as the forest, endless as these long nights of winter and yet that ghastly sadness, that mourning for irremediable appetites, can never move the heart for not one phrase in it hints at the possibility of redemption.

Her brothers searched the outhouses and the haystacks but never found any remains so the sensible girl dried her eyes and found herself another husband not too shy to piss into a pot, who spent the nights indoors. She gave him a pair of bonny babies and all went right as a trivet, until, one freezing night, the night of the solstice, the hinge of the year when things do not fit together as well as they should, the longest night, her first good man came home again.

A great thump on the door announced him as she was stirring the soup for the father of her children and she knew him the minute she lifted the latch although it was years, years since she'd worn black for him and now he was in rags and his hair hung down his back and hadn't seen a comb for years, alive with lice, and his face had very little human left in it, all pity pared away.

'Here I am, home again, missus,' he said. 'Get me my bowl of cabbage and be quick about it.'

Then her second husband came in with the wood for the fire and when the first one saw she'd slept with another man and, worse, clapped his red eyes on her little children who'd crept into the kitchen to see what all the noise was about, he shouted out: 'I wish I were a wolf again, to teach this whore a lesson!' So a wolf he instantly became, and tore off the eldest boy's right hand before they chopped him up with the hatchets they used for chopping logs. But when the wolf lay bleeding and gasping its last, the pelt peeled off again and he was just as he had been, years ago, when he ran away from his marriage bed.

A witch from up the valley once turned a whole wedding party into wolves because the groom settled on another girl. She used to order them to visit her, at nights, from spite, and they would sit and howl around her cottage for her, serenading her with their misery.

There was a hunter, once, hereabouts, that trapped a wolf in a pit. This wolf had been a great slaughterer of sheep and goats, had eaten up a mad old man who used to live by himself in a hut half-way up the mountain and sing to Jesus all day, had pounced on a shepherdess who'd made such a commotion men came with rifles and scared him away and tried to track him into the forest but he was a cunning wolf and easily gave them the slip. So this hunter dug a pit and put a duck in it, for bait, all alive-oh; and he covered the pit with straw smeared with wolf-dung and waited. Quack, quack! went the duck and a wolf came slinking out of the forest; he was a big one, a heavy one, he weighed as much as a grown man and the straw gave way beneath him – into the pit he tumbled. The hunter jumped down after him, slit his throat, cut off all his paws for a trophy.

And then no wolf at all lay in front of the hunter but the bloody trunk of a man, headless, footless, dead.

Old wives think it some protection to throw a hat or apron at the werewolf.

They say there's an ointment the devil gives you that turns you into a wolf the minute you rub it on; or, he was born feet first and had a wolf for his father and his torso is a man's but his legs and genitals are a wolf's. And he has a wolf's heart.

Seven years is your werewolf's natural span but if you burn his human clothing you condemn him to wolfishness for the rest of his life.

By those eyes, those phosphorescent eyes, you know him; those eyes of the werewolf's shape alone unchanged by metamorphosis.

Before he can become a wolf, the lycanthrope strips stark naked. If you spy a naked man among the pines, my bonny, run as if the devil were after you.

It is midwinter and the robin, the friend of man in his bloodstained waistcoat, sits on the handle of the gardener's spade and sings. It is the worst time in all the year for wolves, but this stubborn child insists she will go off through the wood, she is quite sure the wild beasts cannot harm her although, well-warned, she lays an enormous knife in the basket her mother has packed with cheeses. There is a bottle of harsh liquor distilled from brambles; some of the flat oatcakes they bake on the hearthstone; a pot or two of jam. The flaxen-haired girl will take these delicious gifts to a reclusive grandmother so old the burden of her years is crushing her to death. Granny lives two hours' drudge through the winter woods; the child wraps herself up in her thick cloak of bright red wool and draws the hood over her head. She steps into her stout wooden clogs, she is ready. She is a bud, a beauty and it is Christmas Eve, not quite the shortest day of the year; hasn't the malign door of the solstice swung shut, already?

Children do not stay young, long, in this savage country. They have no toys to play with, work hard, grow wise. But because this one was so pretty and the youngest of her family, a little late-comer, she'd been indulged by her mother and the grandmother, who'd spun and woven and dyed the scarlet cloak for her that, today, will have the ominous if brilliant look of blood upon snow. Her breasts have just begun to swell; her hair is like lint, so fair it hardly makes a shadow on her pale forehead; her cheeks are an emblemmatic scarlet and white and she has just started her woman's bleeding, the clock inside her that will strike, henceforward, once a month, until she is as old as the doting granny she has set her heart on visiting although her breath smokes in plumes on the freezing air of a world all covered with snow.

She is an unbroken egg, she is a sealed vessel, she has inside her a magic space the entrance of which is shut tight with a plug of membrane, she is a closed system, she does not know how to shiver. Besides, she has her knife and she is not afraid of anything.

Her father might forbid her, if he were home, but he is far away in the forest, gathering wood, and her mother can deny her nothing; the daughter is imperious as only someone who has always been loved can be.

The forest closed upon her like a pair of jaws.

There is always something to look at in the forest, even in the middle of winter – the huddled mounds of birds, succumbed to the lethargy of the season, heaped on the creaking boughs and too forlorn to sing; the lurid frills of the winter fungi on the blotched trunks of the trees; the cuneiform slots of rabbits and deer, the herringbone tracks of the birds; a hare as lean as a rasher of bacon streaking across the path where the thin sunlight dapples the russet brakes of last year's braken.

When she heard the freezing howl of a distant wolf, her practised hand sprang to the handle of her knife but she saw no sign of a wolf at all, nor of a naked man, either, but then she heard a clattering among the brushwood and there sprang onto the path a fully clothed one, a very handsome young one, in the loden cape and wideawake hat of a hunter, laden with bright brown carcasses of game birds. She had her hand on her knife at the first rustle of twigs but he laughed with a flash of white teeth when he saw her and made her a little bow; she'd never seen such a fine fellow before, not among the rustic clowns of her native village. So on they went together, through the thickening light of the afternoon.

Soon they were laughing and joking like old friends. When he offered to carry her basket, she gave it to him although her knife was in it because he told her his rifle would protect them. As the day darkened, it began to snow again, she felt the first flakes settle on her eyelashes but now there was only half a mile to go and there would be a fire, and hot tea, and a welcome, a warm one, surely, for the dashing huntsman as well as for herself.

This young man had a remarkable object in his pocket. It was a compass. She looked at the little round glass face in the palm of his hand and watched the wavering needle with a vague wonder. He assured her this compass had taken him safely through the wood on his hunting trip, because the needle always told him with perfect accuracy where the north was. She could not believe it; she knew she should never leave the path on the way through the wood, or else she would be lost instantly. He laughed at her again; gleaming trails of spittle clung to his teeth. He said, if he plunged off the path into the forest that surrounded them, he could guarantee to arrive at her grandmother's house a good quarter of an hour before she did, plotting his way through the undergrowth with his compass, while she trudged the long way, along the winding path.

'Well, I don't believe you. Besides, aren't you afraid of the wolves?'

He only tapped the gleaming butt of his rifle and grinned.

'Is it a bet, then?' he asked her. 'Shall we make a game of it? What will you give me if I get to grandmother's house before you?'

'What would you like?' she asked.

'I'd like a kiss.'

She lowered her eyes and blushed.

Commonplaces of a rustic seduction.

He went off through the undergrowth and took her basket with him but she forgot to be afraid of the beasts, although now the moon was rising, for she wanted to dawdle on her way to make sure the handsome young man would win his wager.

Grandmother's house stood by itself a little way out of the village. Lamplight spilled over the kitchen garden where the freshly falling snow blew about in eddies and the young man stepped delicately up the snowy path to the door, as if he

16

were reluctant to get his feet wet, swinging his bundle of game and the basket and humming a little tune to himself.

There is a faint trace of blood on his chin, he has been snacking on his catch.

He rapped upon the panels with his knuckles.

Aged and frail, granny is three quarters succumbed to the mortality the aches in her bones promise her and almost ready to do so. A boy came from the village to build up her hearth an hour ago and the kitchen crackles with busy firelight, she is as snug and warm as the fire can keep her when her blood is so thin. She has her bible for company, she is a pious old woman. She is propped up on several pillows in the bed set into the wall, peasant fashion, under the patchwork quilt she made before she was married, more years ago than she cares to remember. Two china spaniels with livercoloured blotches on their coats and black noses sit on either side of the fireplace. There is a bright rug of woven rags on the pantiles. The grandfather clock ticks away her eroding time and strikes upon the hour.

We keep the wolves outside by living well.

He rapped upon the panels with his hairy knuckles.

'It is your granddaughter,' he mimicked in a high soprano. 'Lift up the latch and walk in, my darling.'

You can tell them by their eyes, eyes of a beast of prey, nocturnal, devastating eyes red as a wound; you can hurl your bible at him and your apron after, granny, you thought that such a sure prophylactic against these infernal vermin . . . now call on Christ and his mother and all the angels in heaven to protect you but it won't do you any good.

His feral muzzle is sharp as a knife; he drops his golden burden of gnawed pheasants on the table and puts down your dear girl's basket, too. Oh, my god, what have you done with her?

Off with his disguise – the cloak of forest-coloured cloth, the hat with the feather tucked into the ribbon; the matted hair streams down the white shirt and she can see the lice moving. The sticks on the hearth shift and crackle but night and the forest has come into the kitchen, bringing its own darkness tangled in its hair while snow settles on the windowpane like a swarm of white bees.

He strips off his shirt. A crisp stripe of hair runs down his belly, his nipples are ripe and dark as poison fruit but he's thin, so thin you could count the ribs under his skin if only he gave you the time. He strips off his trousers and she can see how hairy his legs are. His genitals, huge. Ah! huge.

The last thing the old woman saw in this world was a young man, naked as a stone, eyes like cinders, approaching her bed.

Distantly, a callous howling.

The wolf is carnivore incarnate.

When he had finished with her, he licked his chops and quickly dressed himself again, until he was just as he had been when he came through her door. He burned the hair in the fireplace and wrapped the bones up in a napkin that he hid away in the wooden chest in which he found a clean pair of sheets. These he carefully put on the bed instead of the tell-tale, stained ones he stowed away in the laundry basket. He plumped up the pillows and shook out the patchwork quilt, he picked up the bible from the floor, though not without a shudder, and laid it on the table, marking the place where he closed it with a pheasant's feather. All was as it had been before, except that grandmother was gone. The sticks twitched in the grate, the clock ticked and the young man sat patiently beside the fire, wound about in granny's shawl so you would not have been able to tell the difference.

Rat-a-tap-tap.

'Who's there?' he quavers, mimicking granny's antique falsetto.

'Only your granddaughter.'

When she came in, bringing with her a flurry of snow that melted on the tiles like tears, he flung off the deceitful shawl, sprang to the door and pressed up against it, soe she could not get out.

The girl looked round the room and saw there was not even the indentation of a head on the smooth cheek of the pillow, and how, for the first time she'd seen it so, the bible lay closed on the table. She wanted her knife from her basket but she dared hot reach for it because his eyes were fixed upon her – huge eyes that now seemed to shine with a unique, interior luminescence, eyes the size of saucers, saucers full of Greek fire, an infernal phosphorescence.

'What big eyes you have.'

'All the better to see you with.'

No trace at all of the old woman except for a tuft of white

hair that had caught in the bark of an unburned log. When the girl saw that, she knew she was in danger of death.

'Where is my grandmother?'

'There's nobody at home but we two, my darling.'

Now a great howling rose up all around them, near, very near, as close as the kitchen garden, the howling of a multitude of wolves; she shivered, in spite of the scarlet cloak she pulled more closely round herself that cast shadows red as fire on her transparent face.

'Who has come to sing us carols?' she said.

'Those are the voices of my brothers, darling; I love the company of wolves. Look out of the window and you'll see them.'

Snow half-caked the lattice window and she opened it to look out into the garden. A blast of cold air drove into the kitchen, so that the fire roared. It was a white night of moon and snow; the blizzard whirled around the gaunt, grey beasts who squatted on their haunches among the rows of winter cabbage, pointing their lean snouts to the moon and howling as if their hearts would break. Ten wolves; twenty wolves – so many wolves she could not count them, howling in concert as if demented or deranged. Their eyes reflected the light from the kitchen and shone like a hundred candles.

'A hundred candles on a Christmas tree,' she said. 'And it is very cold, poor things. No wonder they howl so.'

She closed the window on the wolves' baleful threnody and pushed back her hood; she took off her scarlet cloak, the colour of poppies, the colour of sacrifices, the colour of her menses and, since her fear did her no good, she ceased to be afraid. She shook out her hair that was almost as white as the snow outside, it flew out about her.

'What shall I do with my cloak?'

'Throw it on the fire, my dear one. You won't be needing it.'

She bundled up the cloak and threw it on the blaze, which instantly consumed it. Then she drew her blouse over her head; the white skin of her revealed breasts irradiated the room.

'What shall I do with my blouse?'

'Into the fire with it, too, my pet.'

The thin muslin flew up the chimney like a magic bird and now off came her skirt and her woollen stockings and onto the fire they went, too, and were gone for good. So she stepped out of her clogs and ran lightly across the room to the man with red eyes and the unkempt mane in which the lice moved; she stood up on tiptoe and unbuttoned the collar of his shirt.

'What big arms you have.'

'All the better to hug you with.'

Every wolf in the world now howled a prothalamion outside the window as he obtained the kiss she owed him.

'What big teeth you have!'

She saw how his jaw began to slaver and the room was full of the noise of the forest's liebestod but the wise child never flinched, even when he answered:

'All the better to eat you with.'

The girl burst out laughing, at that; she knew she was nobody's meat. She laughed at him full in the face, with its high cheekbones and eyes that glowed in the dark. She ripped off his shirt for him and flung it into the fire, in the fiery wake of her own discarded clothing. The kitchen flamed with light and the old bones under the bed set up a terrible racket of clattering but she did not pay them any heed.

The worst wolves are hairy on the inside.

Carnivore incarnate, only immaculate flesh appeases him.

He will lay his fearful head on her lap and she will pick the lice from his pelt and perhaps she will put them into her mouth and eat them, as he will bid her, as she would do in any savage marriage ceremony.

The blizzard will die down.

The blizzard died down, leaving the mountains as randomly covered with snow as if a blind woman had thrown a tablecloth over them. The upper branches of the forest pines were limed and creaking with the fall, snowlight, moonlight, a confusion of paw-prints.

All silent, all still.

Midnight, and the clock strikes. It is Christmas Day, the werewolves' birthday, the door of the solstice still wide enough open to let them all slink through.

See! sweet and sound she sleeps in granny's bed, between the paws of the tender wolf.

J.G.BALLARD

THE DEAD TIME

WITHOUT WARNING, as if trying to confuse us, the Japanese guarding our camp had vanished. I stood by the open gates of the camp with a group of fellow-internees, staring in an almost mesmerised way at the deserted road and at the untended canals and paddy-fields that stretched on all sides to the horizon. The guard-house had been abandoned. The two Japanese sentries who usually waved me away whenever I tried to sell them cigarettes had given up their posts and and fled with the remainder of the military police to their barracks in Shanghai. The tyre-prints of their vehicles were still clearly visible in the dust between the gate-posts.

Perhaps even this hint at the presence of Japanese who had imprisoned us for three years was enough to deter us from crossing the line into the silent world outside the camp. We stood together in the gateway, trying to straighten our shabby clothing and listening to the children playing in the compound. Behind the nearest of the dormitory blocks several women were hanging out their morning's washing, as if fully content to begin another day's life in the camp. Yet everything was over!

Although the youngest of the group – I was then only twenty – on an impulse I casually stepped forward and walked into the centre of the road. The others watched me as I turned to face the camp. Clearly they half-expected a shot to ring out from somewhere. One of them, a consultant engineer who had known my parents before the war separated us, raised his hand as if to beckon me to safety.

The faint drone of an American aircraft crossed the empty bank of the river half a mile away. It flew steadily towards us, no more than a hundred feet above the paddy-fields, the young pilot sitting forward over his controls as he peered down at us. Then he rolled his wings in a gesture of greeting and altered course for Shanghai.

Their confidence restored, the others were suddenly around me, laughing and shouting as they set off down the road. Six hundred yards away was a Chinese village, partly hidden by the eroded humps of the burial mounds built on the earth causeways that separated the paddies. Already substantial supplies of rice beer had been brought back to the camp. For all our caution, we were not the first of the internees to leave the camp. A week earlier, immediately after the news of the Japanese capitulation, a party of merchant seamen had climbed through the fence behind their block and walked the eight miles to Shanghai. There they had been picked up by the Japanese gendarmerie, held for two days and returned to the camp in a badly beaten state. So far all the others who had reached Shanghai – whether, like myself, searching for relations, or trying to check up on their businesses – had met with the same fate.

As we strode towards the village, now and then looking back at the curious perspectives of the camp receding behind us, I watched the paddies and canals on either side of the road. In spite of everything I had heard on the radio broadcasts, I was still not certain that the war was over. During the past year we had listened more or less openly to the various radios smuggled into the camp, and had followed the progress of the American forces across the Pacific. We had heard detailed accounts of the atom-bomb attacks – Nagasaki was little more than 500 miles from us – and of the Emperor's call for capitulation immediately after. But at our camp, eight miles to the east of Shanghai at the mouth of the Yangtse, little had changed. Large numbers of American aircraft crossed the sky unopposed, no longer taking part in any offensive action, but we soon noticed that none had landed at the military airfield adjacent to our camp. Dwindling but still substantial numbers of Japanese troops held the landscape, patrolling the airfield perimeter, the railway lines and roads to Shanghai. Military police continued to guard the camp, as if guaranteeing our imprisonment through whatever peace might follow, and kept little more than their usual distance from the two thousand internees. Paradoxically, the one positive sign was that since the Emperor's broadcast no food had arrived for us.

Hunger, in fact, was my chief reason for leaving the camp. In the confusion after Pearl Harbor I had been separated from my parents by the Japanese occupation authorities and imprisoned in a stockade in the centre of Shanghai reserved for male Allied nationals. Eighteen months later, when the American bombing began, the stockade was closed and the prisoners scattered at random among the cluster of large camps for families with children in the countryside surrounding Shanghai. My parents and young sister had spent the war in another of these some twenty miles to the west of the city. Although their condition was probably as bad as my own I was convinced that once I reached them everything would be well.

'The place is empty. They must have cleared out with everything overnight.'

At the entrance to the village the man next to me, a garage owner from Shanghai, pointed to the abandoned houses. Catching our breath after the brisk walk, we gazed down at the empty alleys and shuttered windows. Not a Chinese was in sight, though only the previous afternoon they had been doing a profitable trade with groups of internees from the camp, bartering rice-beer for watches, shoes and fountain pens.

While the others conferred, I wandered away to the ruins of a ceramics factory on the outskirts of the village. Perhaps under the impression that its kilns were some sort of military installation, the Americans had bombed the factory again and again. A few of the buildings were still standing, but the courtyards were covered with thousands of pieces of broken crockery. Uncannily, these seemed to have been sorted out into various categories of table-ware. I walked across a carpet of porcelain soup spoons, all too aware of the fact that the only noise in this entire landscape was coming from my feet.

For the villagers to have left so suddenly, after all their struggles through the war, could only mean that they were frightened of something they were sure would take place in their immediate locality. During the past year they had attached themselves to our camp, selling a few eggs through the barbed wire and later, when they themselves began to be hungry, trying to break through the fences in order to steal the tomatoes and root-crops which the internees grew on every square foot of vacant soil. At one time we had recruited the Japanese guards to help us strengthen the wire to keep out these pilferers. In the last months the circle of starving or ailing older villagers planted outside the camp gates – none were ever admitted, let alone fed – grew larger every day.

Yet for some reason they had all gone. As I walked back from the factory perimeter my companions were discussing the best route across the paddy-fields to Shanghai. They had ransacked several of the houses and were now sitting on the piles of broken crockery with bottles of rice beer. I remembered the rumours we had heard that before they surrendered the Japanese planned to slaughter their civilian prisoners.

I looked back along the road to the camp, aware of its curious confusion of vulnerability and security. The water-tower and three-storey concrete blocks seemed to rise from the lines of burial mounds. The camp had been a Chinese middle school. We had arrived after dark, and I had never seen it from the outside before, just as I had never physically entered the empty landscape surrounding the camp which had been an intimate part of my life all these years.

I listened to my companions' increasingly random discussion. Apart from the consultant engineer and the garage owner, there were two Australian seamen and a hotel barman. Already I was certain that they had no idea of the hazards facing them, and that as long as I remained with them I would never reach my parents. Their one intention was to get drunk in as many as possible of the dozens of villages between here and Shanghai.

Five minutes after I left them, however, as I walked back along the road to the camp, I heard the sounds of a Japanese military truck coming behind me from the village. Armed soldiers of the gendarmerie leaned on the cabin above the driver, guarding my five former companions who sat on the floor on either side of the tailgate. Their faces had an ashen and toneless look, like those of men woken abruptly from sleep. Alone of them, an Australian seaman glanced up from his bound wrists and stared at me, as if failing to recognise who I was.

I continued to walk towards the camp, but the truck stopped in front of me. None of the soldiers spoke or even beckoned me to climb aboard, and already I knew that we were not being given a lift back to the camp.

Without thinking, I had a sudden presentiment of death, not of my own but of everyone else around me.

FOR THE next three days we were held in the gendarmerie barracks attached to the military airfield, where some hundred or so allied aircrew shot down during the air attacks on Shanghai had been concentrated in an attempt to dissuade the American bombers from strafing the hangars and runways. To my relief, we were not mistreated. The Japanese sat around listlessly, no longer interested in us and gazing up in a melancholy way at the American aircraft which endlessly crossed the sky. Already supplies were being parachuted into our camp. From the window of our cell we could see the coloured canopies falling past the water-tower.

Clearly the war was over, and when a gendarmerie sergeant released us from the cell and ordered us into the barracks square I took for granted that we were about to be turned loose at the airfield gates. Instead, we were put aboard the same truck that had brought us here and driven under guard to the nearby railway station that served as a military depot on the Shanghai-Nanking line.

The first to jump down from the truck, I looked around at the ruined station buildings, well aware that the last train had stopped here some two months beforehand. Apart from the aircraft overhead, the landscape remained as deserted as it had been on the day of our abortive escape. On all sides was the debris of war – rusting trucks, a paddy-field used as a dump for worn-out tyres, a line of tank ditches half-filled with water that ran towards a small football stadium set back from the road, a blockhouse covered with leaking sand-bags built at the entrance to the station. But the Chinese had gone, vacating the landscape as if at last deciding to leave us to our own resources, to whatever pointless end we cared to make.

'It looks as if we're going to play soccer,' one of the Australian seamen called back to the others as he and I followed the three guards towards the stadium.

'Some stunt for the Red Cross,' someone else commented. 'Afterwards, make sure they take us back to the camp.'

But already I could see into the stadium, and had realised that whatever else took place, we would not be playing football. We climbed the concrete entrance tunnel into the ground, a circle of yellowing grass in the centre of which two trucks were parked. Sections of the empty stand had been used by the Japanese as a warehouse, and several soldiers patrolled the seats high above us, guarding what seemed to be a pile of looted furniture. A party of smartly uniformed military stood by the two trucks, waiting for us to approach. At their head was a young Eurasian interpreter in a white shirt.

As we walked towards them we looked down at the ground at our feet. Stretched out on the frayed grass were some fifty corpses, laid out in neat rows as if arranged with great care and devotion. All were fully dressed and lay with their feet towards us, arms at their sides, and I could see from the bright pallor of their faces that these people, whoever they were, had only recently died. I paused by a young nun wearing a full habit and wimple whose broad mouth had only just begun to take on its death grimace. Around her, like the members of her flock, were three children, heads to one side as if they had fallen asleep before death.

Watched by the Japanese soldiers and the young interpreter, and by the sentries guarding the furniture in the stands, we walked slowly past the corpses. Apart from two middle-aged Chinese, a man and a woman lying next to each other who might have been husband and wife, all were European and American, and from the worn state of their shoes and clothing seemed to be internees like ourselves. I passed a large ruddy-haired man in brown shorts with a gun-shot wound in his chest, and an elderly woman in a print dress who had been shot in the jaw, but at first sight none of the other bodies revealed any signs of violence.

Twenty feet ahead of me one of the Japanese soldiers by the trucks had moved his rifle. Behind me my companions stepped back involuntarily. The garage owner stumbled against me, for a moment holding my shoulder. I listened to the sound of an American aircraft overhead, the noise of its engine magnified by the concrete bowl of the stadium. It seemed insane that we would be shot here ten days after the war had ended in full view of our rescuers, but already I was convinced that we would not die. Yet again I had that same presentiment of death I had inexplicably felt before our arrest.

One of the Japanese officers, wearing full uniform under a short rain-cape, spoke briefly. I noticed that he was standing beside a small card-table on which rested two wicker baskets containing bottles of sake and parcels of boiled rice wrapped in leaves. For some bizarre reason I assumed that he was about to give me a prize.

The Eurasian in the white shirt came up to me. His face had the same passivity of the Japanese. No doubt he realised that once the Kuomintang forces arrived his own life would be over, like those of the fifty people lying on the stadium grass.

'You're all right ?' he asked me. After a pause, he nodded at the Japanese officer. Then, almost as an afterthought, he said, 'You can drive a truck ?'

'Yes . . .' The presence of the armed Japanese made any other answer pointless. In fact I had not driven any vehicle since the outbreak of war, and before that only my father's Plymouth car.

'Of course we can.' The garage owner had pulled himself together and joined us. He looked back at our four companions, who were now separated from us by the tract of corpses. 'We can both drive, I'm an experienced mechanic. Who are all those people? What happened to them?'

'We need two drivers,' the interpreter said. 'You know the Protestant cemetery at Soochow?'

'No, but we can find it.'

'That's good. It's only sixty miles, four hours, then you can go free. You take these people to the Protestant cemetery.'

'All right.' The garage owner had again held my shoulder, this time to prevent me changing my mind, though I already had no intention of doing so. 'But who are they all?'

The interpreter seemed to have lost interest. Already the Japanese soldiers were lowering the tailgates of the trucks. 'Various things,' he said, patting his white shirt. 'Some illnesses, the American planes . . .'

An hour later we had loaded the fifty corpses onto the two trucks and after a trial circuit of the stadium had set off in the direction of Soochow.

LOOKING BACK on those first few hours of freedom as we drove together across the empty landscape fifteen miles to the south-east of Shanghai, I am struck by the extent to which we had already forgotten the passengers whose destination had made that freedom possible. Of course neither Hodson, the garage owner, nor myself had the slightest intention of driving to Soochow. As I could see from his manner as the six of us loaded the last of the corpses onto his truck, his one ambition was to turn right on the first road to Shanghai and abandon the truck and its contents in a side street – or, conceivably, given a sudden access of humanity, outside the Swiss embassy. In fact, my chief fear was that Hodson might leave me to be picked up by a Japanese patrol before I had mastered the truck's heavy steering and gearbox.

Luckily we had all been so exhausted by the effort of loading the bodies that the Japanese had not noticed my fumbling efforts to start and control the truck, and within half an hour I was able to keep a steady fifty yards behind Hodson. Both vehicles were plastered with military stickers pasted to the windshields and fenders, presumably assuring our passage through whatever Japanese units we might meet. Twice we passed a platoon sitting with its packs and rifles on the railway line, waiting for a train that would never come, but otherwise the landscape was deserted, not a single Chinese visible. Circumspectly, though, Hodson followed the route to Soochow marked on the road-map given to us by the Eurasian interpreter.

For myself, I was content to make this circuit of Shanghai, as I had no wish to drive the truck with its cargo of corpses through the centre of the city on my way to my parents' camp. Once I had cleared the western suburbs of the city I would turn north off the Soochow road, hand the vehicle over to the first allied command post – our new-found freedom had convinced me that the war would finally be over by the afternoon – and complete the short journey to my parents' camp on foot.

The prospect of seeing them, after all these years, within literally a few hours made me feel light-headed. During the three days in the gendarmerie barracks we had been given almost nothing to eat, and I now picked at the boiled rice in the wicker basket on the seat beside me. Even the sight of the corpses whose feet and faces were shaking loose beneath the tarpaulin of Hodson's truck did nothing to spoil my appetite. As I had lifted the bodies onto the two trucks I had immediately noticed how well-fleshed most of them were, far better fed than any of us had been in our camp. Presumably they had been imprisoned in some special intern-ment centre, and had unluckily fallen foul of the American air-attacks.

At the same time the absence, with few exceptions, of any wounds or violence suggested one or two unsettling alterna-tives – plague, perhaps, or some sudden epidemic. Steering the truck with one hand and eating my rice with the other, I eased my foot off the heavy accelerator, opening the interval slightly between Hodson and myself. But for all this I was hardly concerned about the bodies. Too many people had already died in and around our camp. The business of loading the corpses into the trucks had placed a certain mental distance between them and myself. Handling all those bodies, pulling on the stiffening arms and legs, pushing their buttocks and shoulders over the tail-gates, had been like an extended wrestling match with a party of strangers, a kind of forced intimacy that absolved me from all future contact or obligation.

An hour after leaving the stadium, when we had covered some ten miles, Hodson began to slow down, his truck bumping over the rutted road surface at little more than walking pace. Some half a mile from the river, we had entered a landscape flooded by a slack, brown water. Untended canals and drowned paddies stretched away on all sides, and the road had become little more than a series of narrow causeways. The vanished peasants had built their burial mounds into the shoulders of the road, and the ends of the cheap coffins protruded like drawers from the rain-washed earth, lockers ransacked by the passing war. Across the paddies I could see a boom of scuttled freighters that blocked the river, funnels and bridge-houses emerging from the swollen tide. We passed another abandoned village, and then the green shell of a reconnaissance aircraft shot down by the Americans.

Ten feet in front of me, Hodson's truck bumped along the roadway, the heads of his corpses nodding vigorously like sleepers assenting in some shared dream. Then Hodson stopped and jumped down from his cabin.

He laid the map across the bonnet of my truck, then pointed along the broad canal we had been following for the past ten minutes. 'We've got to cross this before we reach the main road. Somewhere up ahead there's a sluice-bridge. It looks too small to have been bombed.'

With his strong hands he began to tear away the stickers pasted to the fenders and windshield of my truck. Though gaunt and undernourished, he looked strong and aggressive. The experience of driving a vehicle again had clearly restored his confidence. I could see that he had been helping himself liberally to his bottle of sake.

He bent down under the tailgate of his truck and felt the left inside tyre. I had noticed the vehicle tilting when we first reached the canal.

'Going soft . . . no damn spares either.' He stood up and gazed into the rear of the truck, and with a single sweep of one arm flung back the tarpaulin, like a customs official exposing a suspicious cargo. Nodding to himself, he stared at the bodies piled across each other.

'Right, we rest here and finish the food, then find this bridge. First, let's make things easier for ourselves.'

Before I could speak he had reached into the truck and seized one of the corpses by the shoulders. He jerked it away from its fellows, stood it briefly on its feet and hurled it head-first into the canal. That of a freckle-skinned man in his early thirties, it surfaced within a few seconds in the brown water and slowly drifted away past the reeds.

'Right, we'll have the nun next.' As he hauled her out he shouted over his shoulder, 'You get on with yours. Leave a few behind just in case.'

Ten minutes later, as we sat with our bottles of sake on the bank of the canal, some twenty of the corpses were in the water, moving slowly away from us in the sluggish current. Pulling them down had almost exhausted me, but the first sips of the sake bolted through my bloodstream, almost as intoxicating as the boiled rice I had eaten. The brusque way in which we had ridden ourselves of our passengers no longer unsettled me – though, curiously, as I stood by the tailgate pulling the bodies onto the ground I had found myself making some kind of selection. I had kept back the three children and a middle-aged woman who might have been their mother, and thrown into the water the Chinese couple and the elderly woman with the jaw-wound. However, all this meant nothing. What mattered was to reach my parents. It was clear to me that the Japanese had not been serious about our delivering the bodies to the Protestant cemetery at Soochow – the two nuns exposed this as no more than a ruse, relieving them of some local embarrassment before the Americans landed at the airfield.

Hodson was asleep beside his truck. His sake bottle followed the corpses down the canal. After throwing a few stones at it, I passed the next hour watching the vapour trails of the American aircraft and thinking with increasing optimism about the future, and about seeing my parents and sister later that afternoon. We would move back to our house in the French concession. My father would re-open his brokerage business, and no doubt train me as his assistant. After years of war and privation, Shanghai would be a boom city again . . . everything would once again return to normal.

This pleasant reverie sustained me, when Hodson had woken blearily and clambered back into his cabin, as we set off in our lightened trucks. I was beginning to feel hungry again, and regretted eating all my rice, particularly as Hodson had thrown his into the canal. But then I heard Hodson shout something back at me. He was pointing to the sluice-bridge a hundred yards in front of us.

When we reached it we found that we were not the only ones hoping to make the crossing.

Parked on the approaches to the bridge, its light machine-gun unguarded, was a camouflaged Japanese patrol car. As we stopped, the three-man crew had climbed onto the bridge and were trying to close the gates which would carry us across. Seeing us arrive, the sergeant in charge walked over to us, scanning the few stickers which Hodson had not torn from our trucks. We stepped down from the cabins, waiting as the sergeant inspected our cargos without comment. He spoke a few words in Japanese to Hodson, and beckoned us over to the bridge.

As we looked down at the sluices, we could see immediately what had blocked the bridges and prevented the gates from closing. Humped together against the vents were well over a dozen of the corpses which Hodson and I had pitched into the canal an hour earlier. They lay together like mattresses, arms and legs across each other, some face down, others staring at the sky.

To my shock I realised that I recognised each of them. That presentiment of death – though not my own nor of these drowned creatures – which I had felt so often during the past days returned to me, and I looked round at Hodson and the three Japanese as if expecting them immediately to fulfil this unconscious need.

'Well, what do they want ?' Hodson was arguing aggressively with the Japanese sergeant, who for some reason was shouting at me in a suddenly high-pitched voice. Perhaps he realised that I might respond to his instructions for reasons of my own. I looked at his face and angular shoulders, wrists that were little more than sticks, well aware that he was as hungry as myself.

'I think they want us to get them out,' I said to Hodson. 'Otherwise, we can't get across. They know we threw them into the water.'

'For God's sake . . .' Exasperated, Hodson pushed past the Japanese and clambered down the bank of the canal. Waist-deep among the corpses, he began to sort them out with his strong arms. 'Aren't they going to help?' he called up in an aggrieved way when the Japanese made no effort to move.

Needless to say, Hodson and I were obliged to lift the bodies out ourselves. They lay on the bank like a party of exhausted bathers, in a strange way almost refreshed by their journey down the canal. The blood had been washed from the jaw-wound of the elderly woman, and I could see for the first time the image of a distinct personality. The sunlight lit the line of moist faces, illuminating the exposed hands and ankles.

'Well, we can get across now.' Looking down at his drenched trousers as the Japanese closed the sluice-gates, Hodson said to me 'Let's get on with it. We'll leave them here.'

I was staring at the face of the elderly woman, visualising her talking to me, perhaps about her childhood in England or her long missionary years in Tientsin. Beside her the washed robes of the young nun had an almost spectral blackness, which gave her white hands and face an extraordinary glow. I was about to join Hodson when I noticed that the Japanese were also gazing at the bodies. All I could see was their intense hunger, as if they were eager to become my passengers.

'I think we should put them back on the trucks,' I said to Hodson. Fortunately, before he could remonstrate with me the sergeant had come over to us, beckoning us to work with his pistol.

Hodson helped me to load the first ten bodies onto the back of my truck. Then, unable to contain his anger any more, he seized the bottle of sake from the cabin, pushed past the Japanese and climbed into his truck. Shouting something at me, he drove onto the bridge and set off along the opposite bank of the canal.

FOR THE next half hour I continued to load my vehicle, pausing to rest for a few minutes after I had carefully stowed each of the bodies. The effort of dragging them up the bank and lifting them into the truck almost exhausted me, and when I had finished I sat numbly for ten minutes behind my steering wheel. As I started the engine and drove onto the bridge with my heavy cargo the Japanese watched me without comment.

Fortunately, my anger at Hodson soon revived me. I clenched the wheel tightly in both hands, forehead touching the windshield, as the overladen vehicle lumbered down the uneven canal road. To have taken my sake mattered nothing, but to leave me with more than my fair share of corpses, without a map in this water-logged maze. . . . Within half a mile of leaving the Japanese I was tempted to stop and heave a dozen of the bodies – I had the clearest picture in my mind of those who were Hodson's rather than my own – back into the water. Only the nun and the elderly woman I would allow on board. But I knew that once I stopped I would lose all hope of catching up with Hodson.

Ahead of me, above the fields of uncropped sugar-cane, I could see the poles and straggling telegraph wire that marked one of the main roads to Shanghai. I pressed on towards it, the vehicle rolling from side to side on the earth track. Behind me the bodies were sliding about as if in some huge scrimmage, their heads banging the sides of the truck. It was now a short period after noon, and a potent but not altogether unpleasant strench had filled the cabin. In spite of its obvious source, it seemed in some way to be refracted and amplified by the odours of my own body, almost as if my hunger and exhaustion were acting as the catalyst for the process of putrefaction. A plague of flies had descended on the truck, and covered the outer surface of the rear window behind my head, so that I was unable to see if the Japanese were following me in their scout car. I could still see the profound sense of loss in their eyes as they had watched me leave, and I almost regretted that I had not taken them with me. Far from my being their prisoner, it was they who in some way belonged to the bodies lying behind me.

Before I could reach the main Shanghai road the radiator of the engine had boiled, and I wasted a full half an hour waiting for it to cool. In order to lighten the load on the engine, I decided to throw off Hodson's corpses. There was now no chance whatever of catching up with him, and he was almost certainly speeding through the suburbs of

Shanghai for a first look at his garage. Somehow I would find my own way to my parents' camp.

I climbed onto the back of the truck, and clambered among the bodies piled together. Gazing down at the yellowing faces between my feet, I realised that I recognised almost all of them – the nuns and the Chinese couple, the elderly woman and the three children, a slim young man of my own age with an amputated left hand, a pregnant woman in her early twenties who vaguely resembled my sister. These belonged to my flock, whereas Hodson's intruders were as distinct and separate as the members of a rival clan. Their leader was clearly a small, elderly man with a bare-chested body like a grey monkey's, whose sharp eyes had seemed to follow me all day as I lifted him on and off the trucks.

I bent down to seize him by the shoulders, but for some reason my hands were unable to touch him. Once again I felt that presentiment of death I had sensed so many times, surrounding me on all sides, in the canal beside the road, in the fields of sugar-cane and the distant telegraph wires, even in the drone of an American aircraft crossing far overhead. Only I and the passengers aboard this truck were immune.

I tried to pick up another of the corpses, but again my hands froze, and again I felt the same presentiment, an enclosing wall that enveloped us like the wire fence around our camp. I watched the flies swarm across my hands and over the faces of the bodies between my feet, relieved now that I would never again be forced to distinguish between us. I hurled the tarpaulin into the canal, so that the air could play over their faces as we sped along. When the engine of the truck had cooled I refilled the radiator with water from the canal, and set off towards the west.

It was without surprise, an hour later, that I came across Hodson's truck, and was able to make up the full complement of my passengers.

WHERE HODSON himself had gone I never discovered. Five miles down the Shanghai Road, after two further delays to rest the engine, I found the truck abandoned by a Japanese road-block. In the afternoon haze the surface of the road seemed to be speckled with gold, nodes of bright light reflected from hundreds of spent cartridge cases. The Japanese here had fought a vigorous engagement, perhaps with some intruding patrol of Kuomintang troops. Webbing and empty ammunition boxes lay in the tank ditch dug across the road. Unable to drive around this obstacle, Hodson had presumably set off on foot.

I stopped beside his abandoned truck, listening to the harsh beat of my engine in the deserted air. A hundred yards behind me a narrow lane led across a field of sugar-cane in a westerly direction, and with luck would carry me a little further on my circuit of Shanghai.

First, however, I had to take on my additional passengers. At the time, as I carried the dozen corpses from Hodson's truck and lifted them onto my own, it occurred to me more than once to give up the entire enterprise and set off on foot myself after Hodson. But as we turned off the road and rolled down the lane between the fields of sugar-cane I felt a curious kind of comfort that we were all together, almost a sense of security at the presence of my 'family'. At the same time the urge to rid myself of them still remained, and given the opportunity – a lift, perhaps, in a passing Kuomintang vehicle – I would have left them at the first chance. But within this empty landscape they did at least provide an element of security, particularly if a hostile Japanese patrol came across me. Also, for the first time I had begun to feel a sense of loyalty towards them, and the feeling that they, the dead, were more living than the living who had deserted me.

THE AFTERNOON sun had begun to set. I woke in the cabin of the truck to find that I had fallen asleep beside a broad canal whose brown surface had turned almost carmine in the fading light. In front of me were the approaches to an empty village, the single-storey dwellings concealed by the dark fronds of the wild sugar-cane. All afternoon I had been lost in a golden world, following the sun as it moved away from me across the drowned paddies and silent villages. I was certain that I had covered some twenty miles – the apartment houses of the French concession were no longer visible along the horizon.

My last attempt to free myself from the corpses took place that night. At dusk I stepped from the cabin of the truck and walked through the sugar-cane, breaking the stems and sucking the sweet pith. From the back of the truck the corpses watched me like a hostile chorus, their inclined heads

37

slyly confiding in each other. I too at first resented this nourishment flowing through me, meagre though it was. As I revived, however, leaning against the radiator grille of the truck, I was suddenly tempted to release the handbrake and roll the vehicle forward into the blood-stained canal. As a result of committing myself to this lunatic troupe of passengers, ferrying them from the football stadium to some destination they had never agreed upon, I had lost the chance of seeing my parents that day.

Under the cover of darkness – for I would not have dared to commit this act by daylight – I returned to the truck and began to remove the bodies one by one, throwing them down onto the road. Clouds of flies festered around me, as if trying to warn me of the insanity of what I was doing. Exhausted I pulled the bodies down like damp sacks, ruthlessly avoiding the faces of the nuns and the children, the young amputee and the elderly woman.

At this point, when I had nearly destroyed everything I had been allowed by circumstances to achieve, I was saved by the arrival of a party of bandits. Armed American merchant seamen, renegade Kuomintang and quisling auxiliaries of the Japanese, they arrived by sampans and rapidly occupied the village. Too tired to run from them, I crouched behind the truck, watching these heavily armed men move towards me. For some reason, although I knew they would kill me, I had no sense whatever of that presentiment of death.

At the last moment, when they were only twenty feet away, I lay down in the darkness among the circle of corpses, taking my position between the young nun and the elderly woman. The ferocious flight of the thousand flies came to a stop, and I could hear the heavy step of the bandits and the sounds of their weapons. Lying there in the darkness in the circle of the dead, I watched them halt and peer into the truck, arms raised across their mouths. Unable to approach us, they waited for a few minutes and then returned to the village. All night, as they roamed from house to house, kicking down the doors and breaking the furniture, I lay in the circle of corpses. Towards dawn two of the Kuomintang soldiers came and began to search the pockets of the dead. Staring at the sky, I listened to them panting beside me, and felt their hands on my thighs and buttocks.

At dawn, when they left in their motorised sampans, the

flies returned. I stood up and watched the sun rising through the dark forests of sugar-cane. Waiting for its disc to touch me, I summoned my companions to their feet.

FROM THIS time onwards, during the confused days of my journey to my parents' camp, I was completely identified with my companions. I no longer attempted to escape them. As we drove together through that landscape of war and its aftermath, past the endless canals and deserted villages, I was uncertain whether the events taking place spanned a few hours or many weeks. I was almost sure that by now the war should have been over, but the countryside remained empty, disturbed only by the sounds of the American aircraft overhead.

For much of the time I followed the westerly course of the river, a distant presence which provided my only compass bearing. I drove carefully along the broken roads that divided the paddy-fields, anxious not to disturb my passengers lying together behind me. It was they who had saved me from the bandits. I knew that in a sense I was their representative, the instrument of the new order which I had been delegated by them to bring to the world. I knew that I now had to teach the living that my companions were not merely the dead, but the last of the dead, and that soon the whole planet would share in the new life which they had earned for us.

One small example of this understanding was that I no longer wished for food. I looked out from the cabin of the truck at the wide fields of sugar-cane beside the river, knowing that their harvest would no longer be needed, and that the land could be turned over to the demands of my companions.

One afternoon, after a brief thunderstorm had driven the American aircraft from the sky, I reached the bank of the river. At some time a battle had been fought here among the wharfs and quays of a small Japanese naval air base. In the village behind the base there were shallow wells filled with rifles, and a pagoda housing a still intact anti-aircraft gun. All the villagers had fled, but to my amazement I found that I was not alone.

Seated side by side in a rickshaw that had been abandoned in the central square of the village were an elderly Chinese and a child of ten or so whom I took to be his grand-daughter.

At first glance they looked as if they had hired the rickshaw a few hours beforehand and ridden out here to view this small battlefield that I too was now visiting. I stopped my truck, stepped down from the cabin and walked over to them, looking around to see if their coolie was present.

As I approached, the child climbed from the rickshaw and stood passively beside it. I could see now that, far from being a spectator, her grandfather had been seriously wounded in the battle. A large piece of shrapnel had driven through the side of the rickshaw into his hip.

In Chinese I said to him, 'I'm making my way to the Soochow road. If you wish, you and your grand-daughter are welcome to ride with my companions.'

He made no reply, but I knew from his eyes that despite his injuries he had immediately recognised me, and understood that I was the harbinger of all that lay before him. For the first time I realised why I had seen so few Chinese during the past days. They had not gone away forever, but were waiting for my return. I alone could repopulate their land.

Together the child and I walked down to the concrete ramp of the naval air base. In the deep water below the wharf lay the drowned forms of hundreds of cars rounded up from the allied nationals in Shanghai and dumped here by the Japanese. They rested on the river bed twenty feet below the surface, the elements of a past world that would never be able to reconstitute itself now that I and my companions, this child and her grandfather had taken possession of the land.

TWO DAYS later we at last reached the approaches to my parents' camp. During our journey the child sat beside me in the cabin of the truck, while her grandfather rode comfortably with my companions. Although she complained of hunger to begin with, I patiently taught her that food was no longer necessary to us. Fortunately I was able to distract her by pointing out the different marks of American aircraft that crossed the sky.

After we reached the Soochow road the landscape was to change. Close to the Yangtse we had entered an area of old battlegrounds. On all sides the Chinese had emerged from their hiding places and were waiting for my arrival. They lay in the fields around their houses, legs stirring in the water that seeped across the paddy-fields. They watched from the embankments of the tank-ditches, from their burial mounds and from the doors of their ruined houses.

Beside me the child slept fitfully on the seat. Free of any fear of embarassing her, I stopped the truck and took off my ragged clothes, leaving only a crude bandage on my arm that covered a small wound. Naked, I knelt in front of the vehicle, raising my arms to my congregation in the fields around me, like a king assuming his crown at his coronation. Although still a virgin, I exposed my loins to the Chinese watching me as they lay quietly in the fields. With those loins I would seed the dead.

Every fifty yards, as I approached the distant water-tower of my parents' camp, I stopped the truck and knelt naked in front of its boiling radiator. There was no sign of movement from the camp compound, and I was sure now what I would find there.

The child lay motionlessly in my arms. As I knelt with her in the centre of the road, wondering it it were time for her to join my companions, I noticed that her lips still moved. Without thinking, giving way to what then seemed a meaningless impulse, I tore a small shred of flesh from the wound on my arm and pressed it between her lips.

Feeding her in this way, I walked with her towards the camp a few hundred yards away. The child stirred in my arms. Looking down, I saw that her eyes had partly opened. Although unable to see me, she seemed aware of the movement of my stride.

From the gates of the camp, on the roofs of the dormitory blocks, on the causeways of the paddy-fields beyond the wire, people were moving. Their figures were coming towards me, advancing waist-deep through the stunted sugar-cane. Astonished, I pressed the child to my chest, aware of her mouthing my flesh. Standing naked a hundred yards from the truck, I counted a dozen, a score, then fifty of the internees, some with children behind them.

At last, through this child and my body, the dead were coming to life, rising from their fields and doorways and coming to greet me. I saw my mother and father at the gates of the camp, and know that I had given my death to them and so brought them into this world. Unharmed they had passed into the commonwealth of the living, and of the other living beyond the dead.

I knew now that the war was over.

JOHN SLADEK: AFTER FLAUBERT

A FAC' IS A RECEIVED IDEA. IT ALWAYS SOUNDS UNALTERABLY TRUE. ALL FAC'S ARE REALLY NONSENSE BUT MANY — ETHNIC, BEHAVIOURIST, SCIENTIFIC — ARE STILL DANGEROUS. HERE THE B A N A N A S FAC' TEAM EXAMINES THE SITUATION.

Mr Bosch and Mr Jones sat waiting to tee off. The weather, unseasonably hot for this part of Ireland, made them take off the caps they'd bought especially for this holiday and put them beside them on the bench. Jerry Bosch looked into Jones's exotic Irish-style cap and read HONG KONG. Ford Jones looked into Bosch's modified trim and read JAPAN. They caught one another looking, laughed, and slipped easily into a discussion of Orientals: treacherous on the whole, though one had to admire the Japs' business savvy.

Bosch's company made crisps; Jones's specialised in toiletries; they were surprised how much they had in common. Both had families: their wives this holiday; both were off visiting the same ruined abbey; both husbands found the Irish altogether too glib, too French devious, and their own countrymen lacking in backbone. The British economy was a disaster. The drought — a tragedy.

'I understand it's the C.I.A. behind it,' said Bosch. 'They've been mucking about with weather control, trying to ruin the Russian wheat harvest. The floods in Russia, you see, we've taken all our rain.'

'Really? I thought it seemed unnatural, the Thames drying up and all. But the wife read somewhere that it was all to do with sunspots.'

'Women get the strangest ideas! My wife says it's all part of the great collapse of everything. Written up in Nostradamus, so she says.'

JOHN SLADEK

AFTER FLAUBERT

They chuckled over the folly of women, especially in politics. What was really needed, they resolved, was some sort of men's liberation movement. As for Women's Lib, wasn't it just a diversion, taking everyone's mind off the real issues?

'You've put your finger on it, Bosch. We've been decimalised and metricated to death, taxed into starvation, and beaten to our knees by the bloody oil sheiks.'

'Even Iceland doesn't respect the Royal Navy anymore. Britain is becoming an international joke.'

'There you have it! We've lost respect for ourselves. We let the trades union militants hold the country to ransom: the pound starts its long, slow downward slide; and the next thing you know the country's full of immigrants on the dole, grabbing all the colour TVs and new cars they can get. It's *cause and effect*. And no one gives a damn about the pensioners.'

Bosch agreed. That evening, when the two couples dined together, he started to talk about anarchy, and the need for a return to the spirit of the Blitz.

Elizabeth Bosch said, 'Jerry, I hope we're not going to talk politics all evening. We're on holiday, for heaven's sake! I don't want my digestion ruined.'

'Stven kills,' said Jones amiably.

'But so does this, darling,' Norma Jones held up a bite of pink Westport ham. '*Cholesterol.* The number-one cause of heart disease.'

Elizabeth begged to differ. Cholesterol was said to cure cancer. She'd read as much in the same place where she'd read that beans cause blood clots. The safest thing was to stick to honey, yoghurt, and all brown foods. 'You see, white bread is just so much sawdust, and white eggs are anaemic, and white sugar — well, it's *lethal.*'

'But honey must have sugar in it,' Bosch objected. 'It's sweet.'

'Not really,' said Elizabeth. 'You see, it's organic. Like say grapefruit.'

'I tried a grapefruit diet a few years ago,' said Norma. 'But it made me dizzy. I found I was taking in too much Vitamin C. Maybe it wasn't organically-grown, though.'

Ford Maddox Jones said, 'Norma, I keep trying to tell you, Vitamin C is *good!* Haven't had a cold since I started taking it, and you

MR BOSCH and Mr Jones sat waiting to tee off. The weather, unseasonably hot for this part of Ireland, made them take off the caps they'd bought especially for this holiday and put them beside them on the bench. Jerry Bosch looked into Jones's rustic Irish-style cap and read HONG KONG. Ford Jones looked into Bosch's modified tam and read JAPAN. They caught one another looking, laughed, and slipped easily into a discussion of Orientals: treacherous on the whole, though one had to admire the Japs' business savvy.

Bosch's company made crisps; Jones's specialised in toiletries; they were surprised at how much they had in common. Both had promised their wives this holiday; both wives were off visiting the same ruined abbey; both husbands found the Irish altogether too glib, the French devious, and their own countrymen lacking in backbone. The British economy – a disaster. The drought – a tragedy.

'I understand it's the CIA behind it,' said Bosch. 'They've been mucking about with weather control, trying to ruin the Russian wheat harvest. The floods in Russia, you see, have taken all our rain.'

'Really? I thought it seemed unnatural, the Thames drying up and all. But the wife read somewhere that it was all to do with sunspots.'

'Women get the strangest ideas! *My* wife says it's all part of the great collapse of everything. Written up in Nostradamus, so she says.'

They chuckled over the folly of women, especially in politics. What was really needed, they resolved, was some sort of men's liberation movement. As for Women's Lib, wasn't it just a diversion, taking everyone's mind off the real issues?

'You've put your finger on it, Bosch. We've been decimalised and metricated to death, taxed into starvation, and beaten to our knees by the bloody oil sheiks.'

'Even Iceland doesn't respect the Royal Navy anymore. Britain is becoming an international joke.'

'There you have it! We've lost respect for ourselves. We let the trades union militants hold the country to ransom; the pound starts its long, slow downward slide; and the next thing you know the country's full of immigrants on the dole, grabbing all the colour TVs and new cars they can get. It's *cause and effect*. And no one gives a damn about the

43

pensioners.'

Bosch agreed. That evening, when the two couples dined together, he started to talk about anarchy, and the need for a return to the spirit of the Blitz.

Elizabeth Bosch said, 'Jerry, I hope we're not going to talk politics all evening. We're on holiday, for heaven's sake! I don't want *my* digestion ruined.'

'Stress kills,' said Jones amiably.

'But so does this, darling.' Norma Jones held up a bite of pink Westport ham. '*Cholesterol*. The number-one cause of heart disease.'

Elizabeth begged to differ. Cholesterol was said to cure cancer. She'd read as much in the same place where she'd read that beans cause blood clots. The safest thing was to stick to honey, yoghurt, and all brown foods. 'You see, white bread is just so much sawdust, and white eggs are anaemic, and white sugar – well, it's *lethal*.'

'But honey must have sugar in it,' Bosch objected. 'It's sweet.'

'Not really,' said Elizabeth. 'You see, it's organic. Like say grapefruit.'

'I tried a grapefruit diet a few years ago,' said Norma. 'But it made me dizzy. I found I was taking in too much Vitamin C. Maybe it wasn't organically grown, though.'

Ford Maddox Jones said, 'Norma, I keep trying to tell you, Vitamin C is *good*. Haven't had a cold since I started taking it, and you know it.'

'You never did have colds. Vitamin C is deadly. Really, the best thing is one hundred per cent whole-grain cereals and very little liquid. It cures almost anything. Cancer, heart disease, and – they say it cured some of the victims of Hiroshima!'

Bosch laughed. 'What do you mean, cured them? They were fried –'

'Cured them of radiation poisoning. I don't know exactly where I read it, but it's true.'

'Well, maybe. One thing's sure. Most of the food you get nowadays is absolutely stuffed with poisons. They jab chickens with penicillin to make them tender or something. And have you ever read the list of ingredients on a tin of beans? Frightening.'

'But everything's poisonous,' said Jones. 'Even common

table salt is made up of two deadly poisons, you know.'

'But not sea-salt,' said his wife. She and Mrs Bosch turned to a discussion of organic and natural makeup: skin food made from almonds, slippery elm soap, placenta cream, avocado cream, green lettuce soap, egg wrinkle cream, egg membranes placed on the eyelids, elbows dipped in grape-fruit halves, herbal shampoo, banana cream, wheat germ shampoo. Elizabeth believed that all makeup was bad for the skin, and that it was better to rely on pure soap and water. Soap, Norma informed her, was fatal to the complexion, drying out natural oils. But makeup could be beneficial, keeping the oils from leaking out.

Oil reminded Bosch of a rumour that St Paul's was being secretly purchased by certain Middle Eastern interests, to be turned into a mosque. Jones wondered whether the Arabs really considered sheeps' eyes such a great delicacy, after all.

'. . . loganberry cream, rubbed on each night,' said Elizabeth. 'I understand she lived to the age of 86, without a single wrinkle.'

Norma nodded. 'Of course you know the main cause of all skin complaints: constipation. There's really nothing like colonic irrigation for clearing the skin. Oh, and the eyes. My aunt stopped wearing glasses, after she tried eye exercises and colonic irrigation.'

'Sounds like agriculture in the Colonies,' said her husband. 'I prefer to call it lavage.'

'. . . and calling the faithful to prayer from the Post Office tower,' Bosch concluded. He'd been drinking more than the others, and had missed a turn in the conversation. 'What were you saying about exercising sheep's eyes?'

Jones put him straight. 'But I'll tell you one thing, these Paki restaurants make curry for only one reason – to cover the taste of *cat*.'

Elizabeth Bosch was upset. 'Surely not! Surely the RSPCA wouldn't allow it!'

'Little do you know,' said Norma. 'They allow all sorts of horrid animal experiments all the time. Millions of pets snatched off to the laboratories, to be slowly cut to pieces while they make tape recordings of their screams! Ford, ask for the menu, will you? I think I'd like a sweet.'

Over coffee the conversation turned to medical matters: wearing glasses caused cancer; contact lenses were worse.

The new soft lenses – it was said that they had a nasty way of rolling back into the head and becoming lodged in the optic nerve. Bad vision was all in the mind anyway, or caused by maladjustments of the spine. Norma's aunt swore by chiropractors. There was something to be said for faith healing, too, even if it was only a kind of hypnosis. Jerry was building an orgone box, when he got round to it. Had anyone seen those fascinating TV films on acupuncture in China? Everyone had.

Norma said, 'I think Nature knows best. There's a natural cure for every ailment known, if only we knew where to look for it.'

'She's right, you know.' Ford stirred brown sugar into his coffee. 'The animals chew certain leaves and things when they're ill. And what about primitive people? Those South American Indians who found quinine. It's only because we've lost touch with Nature that we have all these big drug companies with their laboratories . . .'

'. . . animal experiments . . .'

'. . . and then they come up with something like Thalidomide! Or birth pills that give you blood diseases, is it?'

'Yes, or analbolic steeroids, so these bloody Russian women can win gold medals all over the place . . .'

'. . . snatch the heart and kidneys out of you before you even stop breathing . . .'

'Homeopathy? I don't know exactly, but the Queen Mother swears by it. Of course they can afford it, whatever . . .'

'. . . all in the mind, anyway. They say if you put your mind to it, you can change your pulse rate and stop a heart attack in its tracks.'

'I've heard that, too. They say you can do anything. Cure a third-degree burn, or is it first-degree? You can even grow new teeth!'

'Amazing, the human mind.'

That subject led them, over brandy, then whisky, on to the psychic.

'Do you know,' said Norma, 'my aunt swears that when Uri Geller was on TV, her clock stopped?'

'Probably run down,' said Bosch, whose amazing mind ran to scepticism. 'She forgot to wind it?'

'She'd just wound it, an hour or so before. And it had

46

never, ever stopped in all the years she'd had it. What do you say to that?'

Bosch shrugged. 'Cases like that I'm not so sure about. But it could be some kind of radiation. Ever notice how you can stare at the back of someone's neck and make them turn round and look at you?'

All of them had noticed this effect. Ford Jones shook his head. 'Radiation, eh? Is that what they say?'

'The scientists have pretty well proved it, by now. ESP, telepathy, whatever you want to call it – they've got it taped.'

'On tape?' said Norma.

'Just an expression, I mean they understand it. Science has proved it exists. But wait, you've reminded me of something – now what was it?'

'I don't think science understands a damn thing,' said Elizabeth. 'Especially when it comes to occult matters. The scientists are just jealous because they can't do it as well. Predict things, and so on.' She turned to Ford Jones. 'What's your sign? No, wait, don't tell me. You're – you must be – Aries?'

He shook his head. 'Leo.'

'I knew it was a fire sign. I very seldom miss.'

'Are you an astrologer?'

She laughed. 'No, I just dabble. But there's something in it, you know. Look at this year – all the earthquakes in Italy, drought in Britain, floods in Russia, economic crises – it must be the planets' conjunctions and things, mustn't it?'

Norma explained that the end of the world was coming in 1999, according to Nostradamus. Oh, the others might laugh (they did so), but Nostradamus was right about so many other things, like the world wars and Napoleon and Hitler – could we really afford to scoff at things we didn't understand?

'Nothing magical about it,' Bosch insisted. 'Nostradamus was just a scientist. Only science has forgotten all the old methods, like alchemy and so on. I think they'll be going back to the old ways soon. Stands to reason. I mean, the Egyptians didn't build a thing like the Great Pyramid for the hell of it, did they? Six billion or is it million tons of stone, all fitted together like the parts of a watch. But that reminds me –'

'I heard they took an x-ray of the Pyramid,' said Jones. 'But they wouldn't say what they saw inside it. They hushed it up.' He began to ramble on about all the inventions science was always hushing up, such as a car that runs on water (oil sheiks bought up the patent) and a razor blade that never wears out.

'Funny you should say that,' said Bosch. 'They claim – the scientists claim – that if you make a little pyramid out of cardboard, and put a used razor blade under it overnight, it'll be sharp again in the morning.'

Elizabeth found that hard to believe. Jones explained it to her in terms of radiation.

'But I remembered what I was going to say,' said Bosch. 'Stones. And tapes.'

Elizabeth asked, 'What's that supposed to mean? Jerry, are – ?'

'No, listen. It's a new theory about *ghosts*.'

Ford thought ghosts were a lot of hokum. Norma had been to a séance, however.

'The theory is ghosts are just images. The original images got embedded in the stones of, say, an old house, you see? Like on a video tape recorder. And then someone comes along with the right wave-length or whatever – someone psychic – and the tapes play for them.'

'Ghosts,' said Ford. 'I think we all must be tired. You mean – ?'

'Sure, take this old place, for instance. It used to be a castle, before they made it into a hotel. The stones here could be packed with images. Words, too. The right person could sit down here and call up every old – whoever it was – that ever lived here?'

'They could call us up, too,' said Elizabeth. 'In the future, say a hundred years, someone could see us and hear every word we said!'

Ford nudged her. 'Don't say anything I wouldn't say!'

'But we'd be dead!'

They finished the evening by listing all the people they could name who were mysteriously dead: John Kennedy, Marilyn Monroe, Glenn Miller, Martin Bormann . . .

Martin Ryle
Pancake's
Latest
Work

MURIEL MACKENZIE

SUCH A field: is it really still to be found, somewhere, in the depths of the countryside? And of the painter, Pancake, what can we say, but that his manner, however vibrant with genius, is perfectly traditional. Perhaps he is a naïf, perhaps on the other hand he knows what he is doing . . . in either case, his work surely signals that much-desired and long-awaited epoch, the renaissance of the representational.

'What, then' (asked the second Academician) 'is the meaning of the disorder which his picture also figures, and can its sinister incursion be thwarted?'

'Who knows?' They began to make their way out of the gallery, they had seen enough, their eyes were old and weak. 'I don't see how anyone could find out, really. It wouldn't be possible.'

BUT NOW two men, Inspector Wainwright and 'Pedro' Hughes, were breakfasting long and late in a market town hotel, in deepest England. The waitress frowned, when she discovered them still sitting at their table. They ordered yet more toast and coffee, and she had to smile, of course.

They were working, independently, on *The Times* crossword. Hughes on the across clues, Wainwright on the down clues. This stratagem could postpone the moment, though not the fact, of their departure.

'Any nasty ones, this morning?' asked Wainwright hopefully.

'No. Afraid not,' sighed Hughes.

They confirmed one another's results and poured more coffee.

'Well, time to set off,' said Wainwright. 'When we have got our bearings.'

He spread on the table a cloth-backed sheet of the old one-inch Ordnance Survey, while Hughes took carefully from its cardboard cylinder a half-sized photographic reproduction of Pancake's latest work. This had given rise, as we have seen, to excited comment in artistic circles. It was as follows.

A MEADOW thick with cow-parsley, its whiteness dustily echoed by may bushes in the far hedge. In the foreground, a river, peaceful, touched with golden highlights, shadow-dappled by overhanging willows. Then the landscape rolled

51

away, there were oak-woods, barns, three rooks flapped heavily against the sky's blue haze. The time was late afternoon, the season early summer, and in all this – the right hand portion of Pancake's masterpiece – no touch of menace disturbed the visionary serenity which was evoked. Change, you would have said, was banished from this realm, as a focus for whose placid vistas the roofs of the distant manor-house would forever gleam.

Something was amiss, however, with the picture's other half. Slimy men clung to a broken gate. A boy and his dog had leapt up amid the pasture, they were running, seeking to ward off, or to pursue. And these elements sadly threatened, both from a formal and from an atmospheric point of view, the unity of the precarious pastoral.

SUCH, THEN, was the mission with which Wainwright and Hughes had found themselves entrusted: to discover the site, and investigate the origins of this remarkable tableau. The absurdity of their task scarcely requires emphasis. What were they meant to do, scour every inch of the country, by heavy bicycle down the little lanes, and then in boots across the meadows? They had spent the winter lying low, in digs in Redcar, Hughes playing the fruit-machines in the deserted arcades, Wainwright laying interminably near-triumphant siege to the virtue of the Calvinist landlady. Meanwhile, their superior officers had perhaps thought of them as exploring the frosty wastes of East Anglia. (Their superior officers, to be frank, had quite lost interest in their progress. If indeed they had not forgotten their existence. No matter.) Then Spring had come, April, May, and they had been seduced once again by the spell of Pancake's work. Let us go! they had cried, one morning. They were only human, they abandoned the project of 'scouring every inch'. They fell back on intuition. They would begin with the Shires, as being more quintessentially English. They began with Oxfordshire, but seemed to have drawn a blank, and would move on tomorrow. They had agreed to mitigate the nakedness of their intuition by means of a 'scientific' (of course quite arbitrary) 'system' based on the o.s. grid-lines. Wherever two such lines intersected in a terrain designated by the map's code as 'orchard' or 'pasture' or 'woodland' . . . thither our two investigators made their fatuous way.

CLIMBING ONTO their bicycles in the hotel courtyard, again they felt tense, expectant. This happened every morning, if the weather was passably fair – they were schooling themselves to discount it, but you couldn't, at least it was hard, the hazy blue sky tugged at your guts, and all the birds of June made you shaky.

Today was the anniversary of their setting out. As they gathered speed, swooping down the first of the day's hills, Wainwright let out a cry of joy, and raised his clenched hands skywards. Then he applied his rear brake, and fell in behind his friend. Watching the wheels revolve – his front wheel, Pedro's back wheel – always instilled a sense of progress, even of confidence.

IT WAS getting on for noon, when they came to the improbably named hamlet of Gock. And there was the Waggoner's Rest, with tables on the village green. Suddenly the sun shone better, as though someone had turned it up. The two investigators looked at one another, then looked down, at the ground, in shame. It seemed that they were about to do it again: drink themselves into a stupor, stumble onto their bikes, veer down the first grass-track they came to, snore the afternoon away.

After all, theirs was a bewildering mission, to say the least. It was highly responsible work.

The barmaid was old and deaf. 'Two ploughman's lunches!' bellowed Wainwright, making the cutlery vibrate, in its plastic tray. He carried the food out and they ate and drank in happy silence. Gock was a nice little place. The leathery old postman, on his rounds, dropped in for a pint of mild, and sat watching the doomed investigators. His lobster-pink-rimmed eyes glistened at them, above his farcical whiskers. He took had a bike, a black GPO bike. Before he went, he inspected Hughes's and Wainwright's sparkling Academy machines. Then he spat on the grass, vehemently. He toured the periphery of the green. Little ladies, little men, opened their doors after he had called, and watched incuriously as he went on his way. They stood in the sunlight and read their mail, then they vanished back inside. Nothing more would happen, today in Gock, except that the chimes in the Norman steeple would strike the senseless hours, until night returned, with its grateful darkness. A phrase, 'the idiocy of rural life', lodged itself in Hughes's brain, as a crumb lodges itself in your windpipe.

'This is a nice little place,' he said.

'Damn,' said Wainwright, who was going through his paniers. 'I forgot my bunion ointment at the hotel. My feet are in torment.'

'I left my anti-histamine pills,' replied Hughes. 'Now I shall sneeze all afternoon, like a cat. Did you notice, in *The Times*, what the pollen count was?'

'It was very high,' said Wainwright smugly. 'Very, very high.'

They began to drink with grim decision, to palliate the bodily discomfort which now promised to compound their intellectual misery. What an afternoon it was going to be. Never had their enterprise seemed more fraught with pointlessness.

AT FIRST the road out of Gock was strangely busy. A tanker from the Milk Marketing Board rushed past, forcing the bicycles into the hedge. The Milk Marketing Board, the Royal Academy: one might hope for a certain courtesy, as between kindred institutions. But no. Out on the highway, mere selfishness invades men's hearts.

Then suddenly they were freewheeling, down, down, into a sweet-smelling plantation. The causeway, formerly metalled, was now surfaced with sand. The roar of traffic fell away and died. Wainwright went so far as to loosen his tie, that the scented air might have freer play over his chest. He pedalled briskly until he had drawn level with Hughes. God, this is beautiful, he said. The two men, tipsy, sheepish as lovers, looked into one another's eyes, and smiled. They were rolling along at a splendid lick. What did they matter, all the trials of the journey, this haven once achieved? A rabbit sprang from the bank, its white scut bobbing. The air was crowded with sticky summer flies.

Hughes, victim of pollen, entered on a long sneezing fit. A chronic sufferer, he was master, as a rule, even of his most violent symptoms. But now his weak arms shook, his grip failed on the wild handlebars, he lost control, and his front wheel swerved irrevocably into that of his colleague.

Within seconds, the two men were lying in the ditch, beneath their wrecked machines, bloody and shaken.

The damage, particularly to Wainwright's bicycle (he had been blameless of the crash), while not strictly speaking irreparable, amply forced the investigators to proceed for the time being on foot. They spent a miserable ten minutes among the scattered contents of their paniers. A bottle of suntan oil had burst open, coating vital documents in perfumed grease. The cardboard cylinder had been bent almost double, the reproduction of Pancake's latest work (they dared not look at it) must be terribly damaged. Wainwright, who had bound a handkerchief around his lacerated wrist, grabbed the map savagely from Hughes, whose right trouser-leg was drenched with blood. He spread it on the road, muttering bitterly, We might at least find out just where we're stranded. Gock, he said, Gock, can't see the damn place anywhere. The sticky map picked up a layer of sand, infuriating as toast crumbs among your sheets. Hughes hobbled about trying to peer over his companion's shoulder. Go away! said Wainwright. Come here! he said, later. Fuck knows where we are, help me rip this map to shreds. It was a good map, being backed with old-fashioned cloth, but in less than a minute they had demolished it. They left the nasty mess all over the place, staggered painfully down the road, carrying only the picture in its crippled package.

'Since Gock's not on the map,' said Wainwright cleverly, 'let's get as far away from it as we can.'

He was learning something, after all, from his travels. If only I had always navigated with such intelligence, he thought, perhaps we would be safe home now, rather than in the middle of nowhere.

THE TIME was later afternoon. Between the foliage of ancient oaks rich sunlight filtered. Rooks cawed in the middle distance. The two lost men stood by a canal, on the borders of a manorial park. All they wanted was a hot shower and a pot of tea. Instead, of course, they were about to stumble upon Pancake's field. But first they had to ford the canal. Hughes, in his capacity as art critic, was entrusted with the reproduction. Holding it high above his head, he slithered down the bank. Soft mud rose up his calves. When they emerged on the far bank, both men were dripping with green-black slime, its stench clung to them, they would never wash it off.

They followed the line of may bushes up a gentle slope. The landscape, no doubt, now began to develop certain idyllic qualities, which however they were in no shape to savour. Ill, tired, malodorous, they yearned keenly for the long Redcar winter, which had left them so unmoved, at the time.

THEY CAME to the expected gate, and leaned forward on its broken-down bars, weeping with relief. The field was white with tall cow-parsley, and at its far edge a river flowed, over-hung with peaceful willows. In the midst of it all stood a man, before an easel. At last, they whispered, as if the final end had come, and they were too spent to resist. Pancake, catching sight of them, shrieked, and began to paint, surely, joyfully. Suddenly from the deep pasture leapt up a ragged boy, and a dog at his side. They crashed through the grass towards the dilapidated gate, the dilapidated investigators.

When he saw their position, the boy's urgency ceased. 'Too late,' he said sadly.

What did he mean?

Hughes and Wainwright tried to speak, found they could not speak. They tried to move, found they were pinned here, pinned here forever.

'Too late. Lured here. Poor fools. Stuck here. Poor sods.' He whistled, the dog came obediently to heel. 'Come on Rover, let's get home to our tea.'

Soon Pancake, too, had finished for the day. He tucked the folded easel under his arm, picked up the completed masterpiece. He hummed as he strode. His face proclaimed that everything was fine. Passing Hughes and Wainwright, climbing the stile a mere yard from where they hung, Pancake, free now of the field, shot a glance at them, and his eyes were bright with triumph.

TOM NAIRN
The English Literary Intelligentsia

MATTHEW FREETH

"*A man with a twitching face is sitting at the writing table near a window. He rises from a heap of papers and gives the tourists a courtly bow. His face is lined, his brow high and furrowed . . . 'Here is one of the family at work', explains the Duke. 'In the passing of these old houses, nothing is to be more regretted than the loss of the library – and with it, the sort of occupant you now see . . . I would like you to look very closely at this individual. His bent shoulders, his pinched and nervous face, his*

57

tremulous grasp of his quill pen indicates that he will not be in contemporary society very much longer. I am not too well up in these matters, but I am assured that without him and his predecessors we should not have any culture at all . . .' "

Nigel Dennis, CARDS OF IDENTITY (1944)

LITERATURE HAS a low ideological profile in English society. There are no official literary academies like those on the continent. We have no set of *grands écrivains* empedestalled in their own lifetimes and reverently quoted in *The Times*. *Avant-garde* coteries and passions are habitually muted, and mostly confined to a ghetto of their own. Debates on cultural principle sometimes surface in *The Times Literary Supplement*; but they are polite storms in academe.

Michael Kustow recently summed up this apparent absence by suggesting that '. . . our pragmatism makes us shy to acknowledge the existence of an intellectual community here', so we find it hard to 'set aside our native aversion to the idea of an intelligentsia (yes, even the word sounds foreign)'. The result is that 'Our intellectuals sometimes seem to lack not only tactics but voices . . . you have to admit that there remains a prevalent quietism in our intellectual life, an evasion of the uncomfortable consequences of propounding and maintaining a position, and a shortage of mainstream arenas . . . in which the real tussle of ideas about what we are and do can happen.' (*Guardian*, 14th February 1974).

Yet the very low profile is deceptive. Without denying the validity of the points made by Kustow, it is important to see that the quietism and evasiveness he diagnoses has a hidden counterpart in English society. To the absence of a prominent 'intelligentsia' there corresponds in fact, a singular and powerful presence of intellectuals in the social fabric. The presence is an overwhelmingly conservative one. Its function is so identified with the archaic mould of England, and so different from the models for an intelligentsia given us by sociology, that understanding it is difficult.

Metaphorically, one might say that there is no very visible High Church of culture in England, with correctly attired Bishops and Priests, and all the formal rituals. Probably for this reason, there is no very striking anti-Church either, no determined and iconoclastic *avant-garde*. But there *is* a formidable and effective low church of English culture, administered more informally by multitudes of low priests. Their real power is as great as that of any State culture has ever been. Does the culture-landscape look empty here? Search more closely: there are few 'intellectuals', but cassocked huntsmen and fiddling priests are everywhere, zealously shaping a national mentality.

Among these low priests of England, literature occupies a special place. In a large sense of the term (one that includes literary criticism, the academic literary world, and a certain amount of modest philosophising about literature) literature is their bible. It has become the element which resumes that moralised romanticism which is the nerve of the English middle class. As such, it has become indispensable to the constitution of that inner police force upon whom the distinctive structure of middle-class society here really depends.

In summary: there is an intelligentsia in England, more embedded in and dispersed throughout the social body than usual; its job is the creation of a myth-world that bolsters the ailing body (the library is actually preserving the old house); Literature is a main instrument in this great task; and it is doubtful if any intellectual class, anywhere, has ever had more natural authority and easy power.

It should be added at this point that it is indeed 'England' in the strict sense we are concerned with. English culture's great social weight has naturally spread into the periphery in innumerable forms. But this should not deceive us either. Eire, Ulster, Wales and Scotland have different versions of bourgeois society, in which (notably) intellectuals have historically occupied different social roles. James Joyce, Dylan Thomas and Hugh MacDiarmid belong to the story (itself complex and debated) of how foreign literature has fed into the English tradition. They belong with Conrad, Henry James, T. S. Eliot and Ezra Pound; not with the history of provincial writing in England.

ONE OF THE FAMILY

"Here is an aristocracy, established and, like the rest of English society, accustomed to responsible and judicious utterance and sceptical of iconoclastic speculation . . . The influence of these

families may partly explain a paradox which has puzzled
European and American observers of English life: the paradox
of an intelligentsia which appears to conform rather than rebel
against the rest of society."

Noel Annan, THE INTELLECTUAL ARISTOCRACY:
STUDIES IN SOCIAL HISTORY (ed. J. H. Plumb 1955)

THE MAN with the twitching face has written a number of
novels. These are notable for their well-wrought plots and
neat observation of contemporary English *moeurs*; more
notable still (most critics would concur) for their solid
characterisation and analysis of motives. While still in the
nursery he indulged in a certain amount of outrageous
graffiti aimed at the rest of the house. But a gradual introduction to the pleasure of the drawing-room removed his
temptation, and he now prefers to dwell upon other early
exploits. Let me quote here from the memoirs he recently
began composing, in the few idle moments of a busy
existence: 'During the last years of the war, a literary
comrade-in-arms and I, not prepared to wait for Time's
ever-rolling stream to bear Experimental Writing away,
made our own private plans to run it out of town as soon as
we picked up our pens again – if you look at the work of the
next generation of English novelists to come up after us,
you'll observe we didn't entirely lack success for our efforts.'

The note of spiteful self-satisfaction has become more
frequent of late. Yet all this gloating over the victories of the
literary counter-revolution seems a trifle defensive and
forced. It contrasts (one can hardly avoid noticing) with the
same man's verse of the past decade. While the novels have
always evoked the gospel of Life (decent instinct, maturity,
etc.) the poems present an increasingly unmistakable notion
of death: a petty, declining England of sepulchral musing
and wry disillusion in waiting-rooms.

In the same period his furrowed brow and tremulousness
have grown much worse, in ways not entirely attributable to
drink. The man is profoundly worried. A note of hysteria
has begun to ruffle the ironic periods of his essays and
occasional reviews in the *New Statesman* – most prominently,
perhaps, in his much-discussed contribution to a recent
Black Paper on higher education. Thus, in perceptible
phases, that conservative romanticism in which his life has

60

been essentially devoted is turning into a vengeful, almost Catholic, reaction.

The truth is that (as the Duke suggests) he is a poor relation of the family. But the tradition he defends is so great, so old, and so uniquely English, that he cannot imagine a world without it. His writing is consecrated to metaphors of a desirable wholeness. If despair occasionally shows through, it is because he sees a social universe no longer worthy of such imagery: a world that has forsaken William Blake. All he can do is denounce the fallen state, and look for some apocalyptic turn of events which might restore it.

He does not understand the particular features of England which have enabled him and his kind to survive so long, and to enjoy the wan restoration of the 1950s and '60s. Like all myth-makers, he lends a universal sense to his metaphors: he thinks his work is about human nature, not the shrinking crisis of English capitalism. But the reality is that the latter process has undermined the pillars of that older social world which was always the hidden object of his devotions. This was the world that fed his deeper imagination in a hundred secret ways. In turn he sustained it with his imaginative works – not by an obvious or fulsome praise, but through the profounder sense of a familial identity and continuity. His moments of angry polemic with England did not break such an instinct of community: one might even argue that, in the long run, they greatly reinforced it. The man's critical essays have the same mark. Their very lucidity, their determined preference for a common-sense mode of expression and a personalised morality, show someone conversing with other members of a family.

In short: the man in the window is part of an old social dialectic; this is the dialectic in which the English intellectual class has been closely engaged with the older form of bourgeois society for nearly two centuries; the effect of that dialectic was to preserve and adapt an anachronistic social world, within the limits of the possible; and these limits proved up to the present moment, far more flexible and moveable than the prophets of various sorts of modernity in England realised.

THE FAMILY LEGEND

*"In most discussions of thought and action, John Stuart Mill
and his like are for Liberty, and I am for Lordship; they are
Mob's men, and I am a King's man . . . Yes Sir, I am one of
those almost forgotten creatures, who shrivel under your daily
scorn; I am a 'Conservative', and hope for ever to be a Conservative in the deepest sense – a Reformer, not a Deformer . . ."*
John Ruskin, letter to the DAILY TELEGRAPH, December 1865

THE CURRENT agues of the English bourgeoisie make us
forget how far ahead it once was, and for how long. This was
the class which made the first bourgeois revolution on a
large, national scale, beyond the city-state limits of Italy or
Holland. When capitalism reached the rest of Europe in the
earlier nineteenth century, England had enjoyed its leader-
ship for over a hundred years. It had already broken through,
demolished all the reality of feudalism, and embarked on a
mercantile conquest of the world.

While the other national middle classes were in the cradle,
the English bourgeoisie was in prosperous middle-life,
already somewhat conservative and set in its ways. An early
start and huge success had left their impress. It is this
archaic mould which was then preserved through successive
waves of potential disruption, up to the present. The linea-
ments of the older, patrician order were (in Ruskin's characteristic terms) reformed progressively against the onslaught
of those lower-class 'deformations' which could have wrecked
them.

The success of this extraordinary conservative venture
needed favourable external conditions. But such conditions
did exist, as part of the patrimony already gathered by the
nineteenth century: the British Empire. More important
from our point of view here, it also needed a remarkable
battery of social and ideological techniques. It was within
this field of forces that the modern role of the English
intellectuals and English Literature was defined.

The problem confronted by the English ruling order after
1789 was as follows: it had to defend and consolidate its
conquests at home and overseas, yet its very progress up to
that point in history had destroyed most of the natural basis
of social conservation in England. The tide of general
conservatism which flowed all over Europe after the Revolu-

tion subsided employed the Absolute Monarchs, the Churches, and the peasants. In England, divine-right monarchy had been demolished by the original revolution and the peasantry by eighteenth-century enclosures; the national Church was a weaker force than on the continent. There was no permanent, massive national army to counter-balance such weaknesses. Indeed, England did not have much of a State at all. The essence of its good fortune so far was, precisely, that civil society had been able to develop powerfully and fairly freely, without the direction and tutelage of a centralised bureaucracy.

Consequently, what may best be described as a 'synthetic conservatism' was evolved to compensate for these deficiencies. We do not have to look at the whole of this remarkable apparatus now. What counts is to notice the very significant part which intellectuals played in it. It is too much to say they were the artificers of the system: that lay rather with the landed gentry and the traditional (or non-industrial) sector of the bourgeoisie. But the system could not have worked without them. They toiled, willingly and responsibly, to provide that cohesive element, that societal cement without which a break in the fabric of England would have been inevitable.

After all, the old landlord-merchant order now faced huge threats. The industrial revolution bore up with it a new and restive middle-class, self-made and inclined to radicalism. Only a little way behind lay the menace of masses of violently dispossessed artisans, and the new proletariat. This was the biggest single social change history had yet produced. The object of England's artificial conservatism was to tame that change – giving way to it where necessary (as no authentically feudal régime could have done), yet also containing it inside the older integument.

The ideological battle which accompanied and expressed this social effort was launched by Edmund Burke's *Reflections on the Revolution in France*. It was developed by the turning taken in indigenous English romanticism – the romanticism that stayed at home dreaming of roots, not that of the exiles like Byron and Shelley. It was in some ways complete by the 1830s, when Thomas Carlyle had become the principal Victorian prophet-to-be of Life against the Satanic Mills and the 'cash-nexus'. By this time the main-stream of synthetic-conservative myth was secure in its river-bed. It would flow on, a mighty family legend elaborated in numberless variants and accents. Each subsequent generation and class could dip back into the glamorous hoard, and concoct its own story about the 'great tradition' – that is, about whatever invincible continuities it needed to imagine, in order to exorcise some new threat of Modernity.

From Burke, Coleridge, Wordsworth and the other romantics the family magic was transmitted downwards, like the secret genetic code of the English intelligentsia. Familiar litanies celebrate the process, and are themselves part of it. After Carlyle, Ruskin and William Morris; from George Eliot and the more heavily meaningful parts of Dickens, through the profoundly significant *Landbevölkerung* of Thomas Hardy, to the Life-enhancing values of D. H. Lawrence; Matthew Arnold's idea of an organic, civilising Culture down to *Scrutiny* and F. R. Leavis's sermons on the identity of Literature and Life. One has considerable choice. This is not accidental but a rule of the game: as long as you build and subscribe to a suitably precedented and earth-bound English Tradition, the family will find you a corner somewhere.

ORGANS OF CONTINUITY

"Our general indifference to political theories; our quiet and respectable adherence to the things that are . . . this propensity has for centuries assuredly distinguished us: we have been very little alive to all speculative innovations in morals and politics. Those continental writings that have set the rest of the world in a blaze, have never been widely popular with us. Voltaire, Rousseau, Diderot, have been received with suspicion, and dismissed without examination: they were known to be innovators, and, that was enough to revolt 'Our sober certainty of waking bliss' . . ."

Edward Bulwer-Lytton, ENGLAND AND THE ENGLISH (1833)

WHAT IS the essential content of this legend-world? And why does Literature play such a great leading role in its working?

The key notion, reiterated constantly in the tradition's annals, is that of an organic community: a supposedly natural *Gemeinschaft* of authentically human relations, where individuals enjoy the sort of rooted sustenance best for them. The theory of organicism was elaborated in Germany. Imported by English Romantics, it found a more fertile soil in the peculiar existential problems of the bourgeois order here. In effect, the real challenge of synthetic conservatism was the formation of an inter-class national community 'organic' enough to contain the strain of industrialisation. The *idea* of such a society, wielded by an energetic and highly integrated intellectual stratum, was itself essential to the process.

What characteristics follow from this idea? Firstly, the organic society of legend is always located in the past. It may of course be fancifully transported into a Utopian future, and the William Morris strain of English Socialism is the obvious example of this. But the real referents and definition lie in a mythical past, dubiously supported by whatever relics the particular critic can lay his hands on. From Burke's musings on the great trees of England to Leavis's on *The Wheelwright's Shop* the same communitarian image endures. There is always a Village Green under siege from crass, irreverent materialism of some kind; the life of significant soil must be saved before it is too late; Literature exhorts us in the correct general direction (sometimes throwing in a few political tips for good measure).

Secondly, the pastness is connected to pastorale. Organic community is (was) located in the countryside, or at least in villages or small towns enjoying a comfortable relationship with Nature. The real locus of this symbol was the old patrician order: England's landlord-capitalists, the merchants they had allied themselves with, and the relatively new agrarian system of dispossessed and enclosed labourers. The myth made it immemorial: a stable society, hierarchical yet human, nourishing to the higher sentiments. It translated the original form of English bourgeois society into Arcady. This imaginary treasure-house of values then served as an ever-renewable defence of the old Constitution, of lordship and crypto-feudal privilege, of the King's men against the Mob's men.

Naturally, casting what became an overwhelmingly urban society into a myth of rusticity presented problems. But the 'solution' of this fantastic historical problem was exactly what the English intellectual class undertook. From Edmund Burke to *Akenfield*, their successes have been astonishing. Discussing the literature of the early twentieth century, Malcolm Bradbury points out that England had long ceased to be a society really associated with 'the stabilities of the yeoman version of England that writers like E. M. Forster or D. H. Lawrence could look back to in the course of their radical critiques of the new order'. None the less – 'a deep vein of rural nostalgia runs through art and sensibility in the period, expressing itself in forms as various as General Booth's rural colonies, the search for a yeoman ideal of greatness, and the self-dependent intellectuals like Edward Carpenter, making his sandals near Sheffield. The persistence of the rural or organic image in literature runs deep, providing almost *the* essential alternative myth for the era, the only outright model of community as opposed to crowd . . .' (*The Social Context of Modern English Literature*, 1971).

Thirdly, the cult of myth-community is necessarily related to an analogous cult of the individual human nature. Culture is the preservation, or the restoration, of an originally better state of affairs. This is true of the personality, as well as of society. While the latter is shaped as Community, the former must be cultivated *for* Community. A most careful, attentive formation of the soul's better side is demanded by the myth. This is the probable explanation of the permanent romantic mania of all English intellectuals regarding education. Childhood is their unshakeable obsession. Both the progressive and the regressive aspects of the school system seem to be inseparable from this ideological element. Is this why disputes over corporal punishment, Comprehensives and Polytechnics generate more passion among them than the affairs of a crumbling State ? Presumable there is also some connection between the mania and the quite exceptionally large place occupied by the theme of childhood in English novels, and by 'children's literature' in the affections of the wider reading public.

Fourthly, and equally persistently, the ideology is anti-capitalist in tendency. It was bound to take the form (in Bradbury's words) of a 'radical critique of the new order' – that is, of the new social universe of factory industrialism, masses uprooted from country to city, urban cynicism and acquisitiveness, red-brick ugliness and un-patrician vulgarity.

It was of necessity anti-machine, anti-money, and anti-city. It was not – of course – anti-bourgeois, or designed to impede the serious accumulation of capital. The two things should be distinguished with some care.

Being an expression of the (at that time) most powerful and ambitious mercantile class in the world, the English Ideology was scarcely directed against the power of property over men. But it was aimed at the industrial revolution – at the new wave of capitalism which, if uncontrolled might prove uncontrollable. It never intended to stop England becoming the world's workshop; but it did aim to inject into that fate as high a degree of conservative stability and rank as history would permit. English industrialisation had to co-exist with the Village Green, and be ruled by gentlemen. Its vulgar rationality and materialism were persuaded into this corset – to an appreciable extent by intellectuals who had glamourized the old order. Once in it, capitalism's delinquent tendencies, its excesses, would be trimmed and kept in order. The uncontrolled growth could bring revolution; forced into a semblance of Community it would be harmless, even advantageous.

In short – the 'unacceptable face of capitalism' is no stranger to modern English ideology, especially in its literary battalions. In moments of despair, the history of modern English letters may seem to consist of almost nothing but resonant denunciations of the beast. From William Blake up to Dr Leavis, the bemused reader follows the guided tour of diatribe and invective: each new generation gives forth its thunder against the cash-nexus. From the steam-engine to the deep-freeze, Satan's assault on community never stops; it certainly never stops being pilloried. From the Mills up to C. P. Snow, wrathful poems and purple passages have exploded on the heads of anyone with an unguarded good word to say about material progress. Convey the merest hint of an impenitent belief in science, economic growth, or motorways: fifty quivering quills will instantly convict you of Life-hatred, dereliction of Community, and the promotion of alienation.

A THEORY OF CRANKERY

"Professor Kocher, who is American, has missed a certain smell

of the Shires in Tolkien's work . . . in a word, its Englishness.
He sees the respectable Bagginses as figures of mild satire on the
bourgeoisie. But they are well mixed-in with bold eccentric
Tooks frontier Brandy-bucks; and one nostalgic light falls
overall: it is that of summer afternoons in the unravaged
countryside of Puck of Pook's Hill, *to which the Roman*
centurion returns finding no innovation more startling than the
elastic in a boy's catapult . . ."

Anonymous review of MASTER OF MIDDLE EARTH: THE
ACHIEVEMENT OF J. R. TOLKIEN, by Paul H. Kocher,
THE TIMES LITERARY SUPPLEMENT, 8 June 1973

A FIFTH important entry in the list is worth dwelling upon.
This is in some ways the most significant by-product of the
English Ideology: crankery. However varied in content, fads
and eccentricities also occupy a definable common place in
the national ideological life: from Edward Carpenter's
sandals up to R. D. Laing, they have their own chapter of
continuity which deserves to be better understood.

The main problem in reaching this understanding is the
complexity of the relations between the belief-structures we
are examining and real society. For definite and material
reasons, the English social world is over-weighted ideo-
logically. And the usual models available for tackling it are
not much use. They are too one-dimensional. English conservatism has little resemblance (e.g.) to the real feudal
world-view, or Catholicism; even less to the blatant historical
examples of an 'ideology' at work, like French Jacobinism or
Eastern European Marxism.

However, we have some clues to the operation. There are
recognizable recurrent patterns in English ideas, which can
be seen as demonstrations of how a dominant strain in belief
asserts and reasserts its primacy. In effect, it is really the
relationship between this strain and the recurrent opposition
to it which defines its importance. But the relationship is
always worked out over considerable time, and always in new
ways that suit the conditions which have altered. 'Superiority'
is in this sense long-range power over the mentality of any
would-be opponents.

The great counter-revolution symbolised in literary conservatism did, in fact, define itself in this fashion from the
beginning. The outward threat of French revolutionism was

defeated by military means. But the internal threat of radical ideas borne by the lower classes was checked and subordinated much more by ideal forces. As I pointed out earlier, the historical situation of the English ruling class with regard to *this* threat was unique. Thanks to its earlier advance, it was the only major social order where the new wave of middle-class upheavals did not necessarily represent a revolution. It represented instead a threat of what can be called (using a term which only came into being much later, when the process had become commonplace) 'modernisation'. In this sense, England of the Romantic era underwent the first crisis of modernisation.

As a matter of fact, it then underwent its first and only crisis of modernisation: that by which the old mercantile order painfully and protestingly adapted to the industrial revolution. There has been no second one. Neither at the end of the last century, in the Edwardian period, nor in the post-World War II decades would it prove possible to repeat the experience – that is, to implant successfully a more contemporary and dynamic form of capitalist production. And at least part of the explanation must be found in the original crisis itself. For that shock had an original and interesting effect on the English body politic: it led to the huge overproduction of anti-toxins and resistances against the process. The story of what I labelled 'synthetic conservatism', the particularly large and functional role of the intellectual class in subsequent development, and the prominent place of literary incantations in cultural life – these are surely different facets of the reaction. A reaction which became permanent, and built-in to English life: try as they will, no government more recently has been able to uproot or neutralise the organs of this conservative hegemony.

'Modernising' opposition to the hegemony has invariably been second-rate and defective in England. The most striking example is still the original one: the rationalist philosophy of the new industrial-bourgeois class, Utilitarianism. This dry, somewhat wizened ideology of modernity functioned as a chopping-block for English neo-conservatism in the first half of the nineteenth century. Its imaginative feebleness, its narrow and mechanical vision of human nature, its mediocre and unjustified complacency – there are the unanimous judgements of historians and analysts. As a

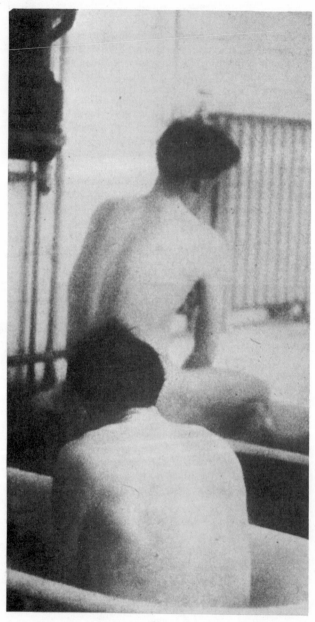

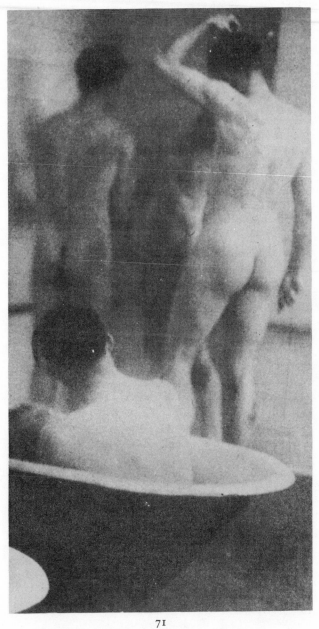

reforming creed it had some impact; as a serious competitor
to the thunder on the right, it never had a chance. For the
next hundred and fifty years, every poet, novelist and philos-
opher knew how to do at least one thing: to refute and deride
Utilitarianism. This was to be the lowest common denomina-
tor of English ideology. The Fabians, in particular, regarded
themselves quite consciously as inheritors: they were offering
a socialist version of the modernising rationale, one which
would save English society from its anachronistic self as
Jeremy Bentham and the Mills had failed to do. England
remained itself. What they did succeed in doing was transplant the elements of a flawed and hopeless bourgeois
philosophy on to the politics of the working class. Our
twentieth-century pundits have sharpened their knives on it
like their ancestors.

The characteristic internal history of the English intellectual is a psychological rehearsal of the same drama. Early
anger and resentment at the irrational mountain of ritual
privilege, traditionalism and sloth; exasperated demands for
a trenchant, no-nonsense treatment of it all ('How can it be
seriously believed that . . .' etc.); realisation, after some time,
that no effect whatever is produced by these barbs – and
that those who persist too long on the narrow-gauge track of
this petulant opposition become themselves narrow and
bigoted; dawning awareness of something to be said for the
mountain; prudent advance into its huge myth-landscape,
where one can quite easily find a corner for oneself; 'maturity'
comes with the first attacks upon the new generation of hot-
headed radicals following behind; the expansiveness of age
brings ever-deeper identity with the Great Tradition, whose
inner meaning is now understood.

How does crankery relate to this familiar cycle? For
considerable numbers of intellectuals, over long periods of
time, it has been the only possible escape from it. The point
is that English ideology, understood in this wider view, is a
singularly complex and all-embracing set of ideas and
feelings. The dominant tendency, romantic-national conservatism, really functions by constantly defeating and
re-absorbing a shallow, limited, unglamorous opposition. It
is the idea-system as a whole one should bear in mind.
Naturally, each new mind coming to it has to spend much
time and effort exploring it anew. In every generation a fair

number see through the weakness of the rationalist or modernising streak ('technologico-Benthamism', to use Leavis's phrase), *and* remain reluctant to join us with the Great Tradition. They smell the rats in the drains there too.

But where can they go ? It is, as a matter of fact, extremely difficult to find any real exit. This is a powerful ideological universe, whose general feel to a resolute rebel is one of almost unbearable claustrophobia. Hence, there arises that peculiar sideways motion – the crab-like disengagement from the system, much more pronounced in England than in continental cultures, which leads to Conway Hall and the myriad of eccentric groups, fantasy-beliefs and cult practices. In the passage quoted above, Noel Annan comments on the paradox of the 'conforming', or non-alienated, English intelligentsia. But of course, the persistent phenomenon of relatively large-scale crankery (especially in London) *is* the long-lost alienated intellectual stratum. Only, the force of the native culture has alienated them into a harmless, pulverised individualism. This particular sort of 'alienation' is almost literal: it results in mildly insane fragmentation, rather than the crystallization of a genuine cultural or political opposition.

In metaphor again, one might say the English idea-system in its whole extent actually does fit the social structure like a corset. Starting off from the terms which it provides historically, it is next to impossible to prise it away from the body. A short-circuit to some other world altogether is the tempting way out. Even a regular few steps in that direction (vegetarianism, yoga, cannabis, Tolkien) gives a little breathing space.

The other obvious antidote to the English Ideology has always been the importation of ideas. Every generation has tried to do this, too. Why should not the deficiencies of home-grown opposition or innovation be remedied by borrowing from international culture ?

The problem is that this process also encounters a huge, so far mainly insuperable, obstacle. For the truth is that English 'insularity' is not a collective psychological whim: it is not – or not only – the wilful provincialism of the intelligentsia which is responsible. This peculiar romantic traditionalism *does* fit a separate mode of social evolution, an entry into the modern world which is somewhat different from the developments that became typical. The culture that expressed

73

those developments, in continental Europe and the United States, has never been easy to transplant (as distinct from importing, on the level of fashion). It has never been very hard to wear a new French hat or extol selected foreign values over the home-grown kind. Forging them into a meaningful alternative, a counter-culture with its own roots, is another problem.

The difficulty is most acute for those who have sought some intellectual defence against the Tradition. Marxism was the inevitable candidate here. But Marxism as a mode of socio-cultural analysis (rather than an economic theory) also belongs to continental Europe of the 1840s and after: it too bears the unconscious impress of quite different paths of development. As if this were not enough – so does the main current of modern *anti*-Marxism, in the shape of Max Weber and modern sociological theory. That current passed from non-English Europe to the United States, establishing only small and belated enclaves in Great Britain. So, the weakness and retardation of both Marxism and modern social theory in England were inevitable.

The counterpart to those weaknesses was the continuing presence of Literature.

THE GREAT BUSTARDS

"Looked at from inside, English society, and its culture and literature, can seem a happy enclave of tradition and liberalism, a living fragment of the 19th century, which, given a minimum amount of intelligent adjustment, might go on existing indefinitely. Yet, on a global view . . . there is something precarious about the survival of English values, for all their amenity: as a cultural phenomenon the country has all the pathos and unreality of an Indian reservation, full of busily cultivated and exhibited native crafts and customs."

Bernard Bergonzi, 'The Ideology of Being English', in THE SITUATION OF THE NOVEL (1970)

'I WHO have been formed in this English idiom . . . fall into a different kind of meditation on social process and individual agency, conditioned by a literary culture, among instances, objections, qualifications, ambiguous metaphors . . .' writes one of the most powerful voices of the contemporary English left,

74

Edward Thompson. His socialism belongs, self-consciously and defiantly, to the native romantic tradition. It is founded on the illusion that the latter's 'radical critique' of modernity and capitalism contains a progressive tendency – a positive element, distinct from its conservatism, which can be cultivated separately and made to grow into a socialist future.

In the same *Socialist Register* essay (1973) he goes on to compare this indigenous socialist culture to the flightless 'great bustard' of an older England: a bird incapable of theory, tied to 'the diminishing soil of an eroding idiom'. That idiom is 'protestant, individualist, empirical, disintegrative of universals', and, of course, literary. Poetry unites English moralism and English romanticism: William Blake is the English inspirational equivalent to Karl Marx.

Thus, the idiom of the Organic Community mythology extends to communism. As Thompson sees it, it will (given some luck) dominate the future as well as the past two centuries. He does not think it sufficient that it has brainwashed the minds of the nineteenth-century industrial bourgeoisie and the twentieth-century labour movement. Reverting to our own ambiguous metaphor for a moment: the great house has an odd out-building, a kind of leaky lean-to over by the stables. Its position is tolerated, although it will never really belong. But it is full of people whose most ardent wish *is* to belong. They have spent much of the last twenty years devising theories of belonging and rootedness: the gist of these theories is that their shack stands for the real civilisation of the house. When the house falls, they will not fall with it: they will become the house.

Why does Literature play such a central role in this incredible ideological empire? Why does the 'idiom' binding it together have to be so largely composed of story-telling, poetic imagery, and their solemnisation in academic Lit. Crit.?

The reason is probably that the peculiar unity imposed upon England by the politico-cultural counter-revolution I mentioned previously has never been theorisable. It defeated – and goes on defeating – reason in two distinct senses. First, it represents a type of social evolution different from the countries which produced 'reason', in the sense of the important theories and categories of modern development. So it has remained quite difficult to apply theory to it significantly at all. There is nothing mysterious about this. Sufficient original effort in the theoretical field could undoubtedly solve the problem; but that effort has not in fact been made.

Secondly – and far more important – there is no will to make the effort. The Great Tradition has positively resisted and ousted 'reason', as something irrelevant, or damaging, to the idiom of conservative romanticism. The only significant exception to this profound resistance was probably the brief episode of English Hegelianism, between the 1860s and 1900. Led by T. H. Green and F. H. Bradley, this was an attempt to impart philosophical system and dignity to the English universe – to frame a theory worthy (as they conceived it) of the moral impulse and social achievements of Victorian England. The fate of that effort is worth underlining: it has vanished from the English cultural memory completely. With it, incidentally, there vanished most of the likely basis for the diffusion of Marxism among English intellectuals (in an other than ghettoised fashion). After 1900, it was effaced by another chapter in the conservative counter-revolution of ideas. This time, a philosophical one led by the intellectual reactionaries Bertrand Russell, G. E. Moore and Ludwig Wittgenstein. These turned philosophy into a harmless anti-theoretical pursuit, capable of presiding over the National Myth-world hand in hand with Literature.

What Literature does, and what abstract theorising never could do, is evoke the organic continuities of English life by imaginative suggestion. Its power is that of spirit-raising – the secular religion of the reservation, as it were, linking together the various crafts and totems in a community of attitude or feeling. The analysis of this belongingness has always been difficult. But the thing is easy to recognise, as is its strength. It amounts to a profound and often quite unchauvinistic cultural nationalism, one which unites cranks and communists, professors and politicians, scholars and bed-time readers, into a tacit commonalty of outlook.

The novel, above all, shapes this *Geist*. In D. H. Lawrence's words, its 'moral work' is to be 'the perfect medium for revealing to us the changing rainbow of our living relationships. The novel can help us to live, as nothing else can: no didactic Scripture, anyhow . . .' (*Morality and the Novel*). F. R. Leavis's vision of the English University is an institutionalisation of the idea. The ruling élite's soul should be shaped there by literature and literary criticism: far sounder influences on judgement than any sort of abstraction. Generalisations are anti-communitarian by nature. 'I avoid generalities . . . because they seem too clumsy to be of any use. I thought I had provided something better. My whole effort was to work in terms of concrete judgements and particular analyses: "This – doesn't it ? – bears such a relation to that; this kind of thing – don't you find it so ? – wears better than that", etc.' (*Scrutiny*, answering critical remarks of René Wellek's.)

'Protestant, individualist, empirical, disintegrative of universals' – indeed. It is all too easy to imagine the perfect day's study at this ideal University, entirely devoted to thising and thating: the Leavisian lecture on aspects of the later George Eliot; then the 'philosophy' discussion of Ifs and Cans, on Austinian lines; after lunch the history hour with a disciple of Sir Lewis Namier ('Bedfordshire Tory Families before the Civil War – Part VII'); in the evening, relaxation at the Labour History Society over a paper on 'Wives of the North Wales Slate Quarry Workers, 1930–1934'; to bed with the new Margaret Drabble.

As many critics have pointed out, lunatic empiricism is the perfect psychological and pedagogic match for romantic conservatism. It destroys the intellect, to render the thaumaturgic power of Literature even greater. By extirpating the slightest temptation to abstract thought, it guarantees the onward flow of Organic Community for another few years.

INTELLECTUAL MACHINERY

"The English writers lived a bounded life peculiarly their own in their own sphere of activity within their tradition which was never accessible to us . . . But none the less, after a few days I felt indescribably satisfied in London . . . What was really salutary was the sense of being again in a civil, courteous, unexcited, hateless atmosphere . . . The English lived more peacefully, more contentedly and were more interested in their gardens and little hobbies than in their neighbours."

Stefan Zweig, THE WORLD OF YESTERDAY (1943)

I HAVE little space to describe the real basis which has underlain this bounded and peculiar tradition. Through it, English civil society has secreted the factors of its own cohesion and continuity. It has done so to an astonishing extent independently of the State – that is, in a fashion quite distinct from the societies Zweig was used to.

Until very recently indeed, English society produced relatively few intellectuals: the population involved in Higher Education at all was quite small. In Victorian times the school and university system was reformed to accommodate middle-class pressures. But these reforms confirmed the class hierarchy and élitism of the old order. In effect, they limited and conditioned recruitment into the intellectual ranks. A private school system and independent universities turned out the quantity and quality of brain-workers which society was ready for – much more efficiently than the bureaucratized and State-regulated machinery that became standard elsewhere.

This extreme selectivity may seem to contradict the major weight I ascribed to the intelligentsia previously. But really the two things go together. State-run, more egalitarian systems almost invariably over-produced intellectuals: this gave rise to the phenomenon of the unemployable graduate, and so encouraged the formation of a politically hostile and culturally restless intellectual stratum (the 'alienated' intelligentsia). By contrast the English civil machinery underproduced its intelligentsia. They were relatively few, they knew each other, and they had enjoyed community with the other members of the new ruling-class. They were, in the familiar phrase, an 'old-boy network' as opposed to a democratic crowd of equally-stamped graduates.

Hence, they were naturally over-employed in society's business. Instead of over-production and unemployment, there was in England under-production and over-employment. This was not merely a question of numbers. Higher education and culture are factors in a larger system of social self-regulation – that complex of subtle mechanisms by which English bourgeois society maintained its equilibrium without recourse to a State bureaucracy. So, the intelligentsia was absorbed in these solid tasks: Royal Commissions, Commissions of Inquiry, Committees on this and that, Voluntary Associations for almost everything, Councils, Societies for the Promotion of Good Causes, prison-visiting, Tribunals adjudicating vexed problems, Magistrates' Courts, the BBC, other forms of Social Work. The coral reef was crowned by the supreme job of Culture-imparting, both in the school-system and outside it.

At the end of his exhausting week, the English intellectual retires with his equally fatigued wife and family to the cottage at Akenfield. There they recuperate by gardening and communing a little awkwardly with the village folk. The evenings are spent reading (or sometimes composing) novels dealing with the disintegration of moral values, or the decline of Community under the impact of Modern Civilisation. Occasionally familiar faces distract them from their books to the TV screen. On the Sunday morning (weather permitting) there will be the usual ramble on Watership Down, climaxed – if the children leave them alone long enough – by a few moments spent contemplating the gentle landscape beyond.

Long ago Elie Halévy stated that nineteenth-century England avoided a revolution because of the profoundly implanted Protestant moralism of its people. This spirit was reanimated, he argued, by the ethico-religious revival of the earlier nineteenth century: this constituted 'Victorianism' in the usual sense, at the same time as the old order was conducting its successful conservative struggle against the industrial revolution. But perhaps he did not describe closely enough how the intellectuals joined the two processes into one. It was this totally *engagé* intelligentsia that re-expressed Protestantism best, with its responsible and energetic devotion to the social fabric – at the same time linking the tradition's energy to an ideology of conservative romanticism. It combined good works with Literature, in a way that endured.

There were of course many other material conditions, which alone made such endurance possible. We saw already that Empire was one of these. Imperialism made possible a limited, rather inefficient industrial system linked to such remarkable conservative superstructures. Then in the era before the First World War it made possible the formation of a type of capitalism whose commanding sector was much more compatible with all the norms of social conservatism. Finance-capital dominance was in this sense the distinctive domestic product of the empire: the milieu and rigid institutions of city life formed organic ties into the whole apparatus of patrician privilege and its attendant ideology. Their survival into the post-colonial period, and their resurgence in conjunction with the general capitalist boom of the 1950s and '60s, made possible the continuation of the English Ideology down to this day. City capitalism – certainly not industry! – created the climatic conditions for the great Literary counter-revolution of the last twenty years.

REVOLUTIONS OF THE WORD?

"Dear Charles Henri Ford,

I showed Blues *to a young anglojewish poet publishing his first book this autumn and he was sniffy not to say snotty about it, ignored the newer names, just mumbled 'Oh Gertrude Stein m-m-m H. D. h-m-m', he turned out to be one of those circular-tourists of whom we have more than our fair share. And the automaton worked according to formula you could see him coming quick to assert his modernity OH he had been ALL through the modern movement, the 'modern' movement being a nicely-rounded-off circular tour on a giant racer, the thrills now comfortably over & its him and the rest of the arty literary crew for the sweet English countryside tea on the lawn or back to this that and the other. Back to mother-church . . . or back to sanity, back even to Rubens back to insularity & the peculiar arrogance found here as of the 'rising' woman sculptor who complained to me of Brancusi he was SO LIMITED & of art critics who speak always of cubist* experiments *and* exercises *in abstraction. There is a sniffy earnestness & superciliousness towards the new thing, a constipated preference for say Virginia Woolf to James Joyce & the inevitable new standard of weakly modern good taste that badly needs a belated whiff of to-hell-with-art propaganda . . . Of the revolution of the word & the dream let loose there is little here. For that we come to you,* Blues *and others*

Yours sincerely,
Sidney Hunt, Sept. 1929"

THIS CRY of despair came from the editor of an obscure English vanguard periodical, *Ray*, whose birth and death had already occurred in 1927. It was addressed in the form of a 'London Letter' to the editor of a comparable but more successful US magazine, *Blues*. In 1966 *Form* reproduced it as part of a series devoted to Little Magazines of the past.

From the 1880s until the First World War there was a varied and important development of innovative culture in England. This modernist opposition to the mainstream conservative tradition reached its peak during the few years prior to 1914 – the brief moment when 'An astonishing group of writers gathered in London and, as a result of their activities there, set in motion what we now call modern English and American literature' (Raymond Rosenthal, introduction to Wyndham Lewis's *A Soldier of Fortune*, 1966). The literary *avant-garde* was accompanied by breakthroughs in other areas too, the most famous being the Post-Impressionist Exhibitions. 'On or about December 1910 human character changed . . .', wrote Virginia Woolf (*The Captain's Death-Bed and Other Essays*).

Modernism had recovered from the drastic blows of the assaults on Wilde and Beardsley, and the imperialist mania of the South African War. It was on the offensive once more, this time in consort with deep new oppositional currents outside the arts. Feminism and Syndicalism both challenged the conservative order while a formidable array of bodies emerged to protect it. In the year of the Post-Impressionists, that 'foreign threat to native English art and essential English morality . . . the image of French unhealthiness threatening English healthiness', there was held the Conference of Representatives of London Societies Interested in Public Morality (the Social Purity Alliance, the Alliance of Honour, etc., etc.). The aim was 'opposition . . . to the moral and social implications of the technique, and to its foreignness' (Samuel Hynes, *The Edwardian Turn of Mind*, 1968). This was a climax to years of campaigning by the National Council of Public Morals, Inspector Sweeney of the Yard, and Dr Saleeby of the Eugenics Society, in relation to which the Festival of Light dwindles to insignificance.

The Great War resolved these social and cultural conflicts. It did not do so entirely in favour of this extreme imperialist right, also discredited to some extent by the carnage. But the post-war compromise (sealed by the crisis of 1926) was of course a conservative one. It was the innovation and the essential internationalism of the old *avant-garde* that suffered most. 'One could argue', says Malcolm Bradbury, 'that by about 1925 the whole movement was more or less ex-

hausted . . . In England, certainly, it was in many respects
declining from the end of the war onwards . . . as the cosmo-
politan atmosphere in England had begun to fade' (op. cit.).
By the time Hunt was writing his London Letter, the tide
had moved towards the reconsolidation of the Tradition –
'to bring back traditional character and plot rather than to
speak the inexpressible', so an American critic has put it.

The new return to Community now had a much firmer
foundation, as far as the Literary cohorts were concerned.
Looking round one now, writes David Lodge, 'It is difficult
to believe that as an academic subject of any consequence
English is scarcely older than the century . . . Oxford did not
establish an Honours School of English until 1893, Cambridge
until 1917' (*The Twentieth Century*, edit. B. Bergonzi, 1970).
But once established, the subject rapidly made up for lost
time. During the long era of shrinking empire and outside
threats since the 1920s, the educational apparatus itself has
played an increasing role in underwriting the Ideology of
being English.

After World War II, a second and still more determined
reconsolidation took place on this stronger basis. Ideology
was intensified in proportion to the real difficulties and
decline. Experimentalism and new attacks on the inexpressible were reduced to even smaller ghettos, even more
prominently labelled 'Foreign'. The general state of mind in
which English Literature still finds itself is perhaps best con-
veyed by Margaret Drabble's firm conviction that: 'I don't
want to write an experimental novel to be read by people in
fifty years, who will say, ah, well, yes, she foresaw what was
coming. I'm just not interested. I'd rather be at the end of a
dying tradition, which I admire, than at the beginning of a
tradition which I deplore . . .' (BBC interview, 1967, 'Novelists
of the Sixties').

Fortunately, some deeper conditions have at least begun
to change during this prolonged period of involution and
complacency. Rash State-sponsored reforms of Higher
Education, in the context of steeper economic decline, have
produced something more like the detached and restive
intelligentsia of other nations. Over-production and under-
employment may at last be reaching English shores. In the
academic world of ideas, *Radical Philosophy* has set a pattern
for numerous other radical protests against the prevailing

orthodoxy. Leavisites and the other *chiens de garde* have sensed the peril well enough: they foresee a rising tide of unlettered riff-raff pouring from the Polytechnics and new universities, new hordes of technologico-Benthamism, potentially given to Marxism or worse in politics, and to seditious experimentalism in the arts. Is it too much to hope that there will indeed be a new era of revolutions of the word and dreams let loose? A new effort to voice the unknown and the future, and to help shape that future by throwing off the suffocating mantle of the English Ideology once and for all?

MARTIN
SEYMOUR
SMITH

EDWARD BAWDEN

A CLIMATE OF WARM
INDIFFERENCE

HOSTILITY TO modernism in England is a phenomenon
neither new nor surprising. People who depend for their
security on faith in external reality – the reality of *The Times*
or the party conferences or Agatha Christie – are likely to be
driven, from time to time, to such gestures as the furious
smashing-up of non-representational sculptures (as happened in recent years at a Barbara Hepworth exhibition).
This kind of hostility, though disorganised and spontaneous,
is reminiscent of the curiously sensual rage generated in
virtuists by the phenomenon of sexism. Just as those pre-
Freudians who fulminate against some doubtless boring
Dane's intention to make a film about the 'sex-life of Christ'
reveal their fascination with the project by giving it such a
degree of publicity that they make sure it will be made
somewhere – they will then be able to see it, ostensibly to
condemn it – so the destroyers of 'modern' art behave in that
very distorted, violent manner which the objects of their
wrath depict. Even the philistine searches, in his inchoate
way, for the real.

84

This is a sociological matter, and almost any literary columnist or teacher of literature at a polytechnic (though not at a school) would agree. But what about the 'enlightened' attitude to modernism in England? Is our fiction modernist? Is our poetry modernist? What is the standard of English book-reviewing? To answer these questions it is necessary to ask what – and why – modernism is. Was there an English *avant-garde*, and should there have been if there was not? Is literature in England now almostly totally dead? And if it is. how?

Is the now exiled Sinyavsky right when he concludes that conventional realism, whether sincere or ingratiating, is an inadequate means of representing the present? Sinyavsky wrote *On Socialist Realism* in the Fifties, and smuggled it out to the West as 'Abram Tertz', where it was published in 1959. 'I put my hope in a phantasmagoric art, with hypotheses instead of a Purpose, an art in which the grotesque will replace realistic descriptions of ordinary life. Such an art would correspond best to the spirit of our time. May the fantastic imagery of Hoffman and Dostoievsky, of Goya, Chagall and Mayakovsky . . . and of many other realists and non-realists teach us how to be truthful with the aid of the absurd and the fantastic'. (This translation is by G. Dennis.) The Gogolian *Lyubimov* (1963), narrated by the elderly historian Proferansov in a style compounded of bureaucratic jargon, the colloquial and button-holing garrulity, is in no familiar sense 'realist'. In the first place, no one has yet discovered, as Lenya Tikhomirov did, the secret of 'psychic magnetism'. But are his 'miracles' real?

For every reader of *Lyubimov*, translated as *The Makepeace Experiment* (1965), there must be at least as many as ten thousand (probably more) of Solzhenitsyn's *One Day in the Life of Ivan Denisovich*, a skilful, courageous, restrained and ironic documentary. Are we right, in England, to give this – not to speak of Solzhenitsyn's later and progressively inferior works – such precedence? Whose 'reality' is the more 'real'?

Is David Caute right when he asserts that 'Britain's best artists persist in seeing things the way they really are' (he speaks apropos of David Storey)? This is a very large claim; but, beyond its evident largeness as a claim, it fails to mean anything at all. How are 'things', *really*! In English letters,

85

I should claim, the climate is one of warm indifference (the phrase was suggested to me, and I accept it as a just diagnosis); and English writing is almost, though not quite, permeated by an acceptance of the death of the word. But this is a diagnosis, not an indictment. What are the historical reasons for it? Why should such a state of affairs exist in a country which has produced, in past eras, such obviously great literature, so obviously adequate to describe the reality of *its* era (Elizabethan drama and poetry; the eighteenth- and nineteenth-century novel)?

LONG BEFORE the notion that the 'civilised' world was perfectly and comprehensively ordered had been universally challenged (the climax came with the Renaissance and its inevitable consequence, the Reformation, but the results were not fully felt until the eighteenth century), certain writers, artists and sects recorded their individual objections. Archilochus rails eloquently against everything. Aeschylus writes from within a system, but demonstrates its horrors. Sophocles, the equal of Shakespeare, rips open the wound of blind, obedient acceptance of any 'belief' by some of the most concentrated poetry ever written. Aristophanes dissolves an 'ordered' universe into a just as richly 'ordered'

comedy. The psychopathic, epileptic, lumpenastralist Paul tries, with a terrible degree of success, to reimpose an order: a sick lie: rigid, closed, an obscene mixture of opportunistic pragmaticism and false piety, whose origin is sexual guilt. This is, as many modern Christian writers (for example, S. R. G. Brandon) have shown, a false Christianity.

But gnosticism, though persecuted and driven underground, provides a clearer picture of the true predicament of man; officially suppressed – it survives in the teaching of Manes, and then in the persistent Cabbala. Today, with the barrennesses of positivism (say, the clever pomposity of Popper) and the hypocrisies or stupidities of institutional religion (say, the recent vacuous clichés of Coggan) having proved unsatisfying, gnosticism, though unrecognised as such, has permeated our lives. Perhaps, untidy and open-ended and fantastic and never organised into a single dogma to be perpetrated upon mankind, it always – at a secret level – did. Christ himself is as likely to have been a gnostic as anything else, as the Gospel of St Thomas suggests. (After all, the four canonical gospels no longer carry the historical weight that they once did: a serious defence of them, in serious historical terms, is no longer possible.) And most enlightened Christians understand this, just as most enlightened non-Christians do not take advantage of the failure of the religion at a historical level.

There are four great early witnesses: Rabelais, Montaigne, Cervantes, Shakespeare. However much we may now reject the body-mind split in philosophical terms, we have to admit that it originates in a phenomenological truth: our minds seem, too often, to be split from our bodies. The 'good' seems too often to co-exist with the 'bad'. We even will this to be so. Reality is not that of the conventional English philosophers, who, pitifully, can never agree about what it is; it is what we experience. Sartre does not want to be a Cartesian dualist; but when Merleau-Ponty accused him of being one he was right. It is doubtful if Kafka, inasmuch as he was interested in philosophy at all, was technically a dualist (philosophical dualism has psychological connections with religious dualism – as is obvious enough); but neither of his two later novel fragments can be understood except against a gnostic-Cabbalistic background. What are those strange beings who claim to represent a Castle (which is not

87

even a castle, as readers would discover if only they would pay attention to the text) if they are not, as Erich Heller suggests, a 'company of gnostic demons, successfully holding an advanced position against the manoeuvres of an impatient soul?'

The Enlightenment was as a whole an attempt to calm down nerves shattered by the vibrations emanating from the Reformation. The eighteenth century produced mostly 'reasonable' works. The deism of such as Voltaire (and, indeed, of Pope – despite his nominal Roman Catholicism) offered a temporary refuge in what was mainly an age of prose, even when the prose was served up in neat and comforting verse forms. The nervousness of some writers (for example, Swift and Diderot) need not be discussed here, only acknowledged. In general, the poetic – the expression of uncertainty, the acceptance of its existence, the doubt if order exists, the search for it – was suppressed.

The seeds of modernism were sown in the shadow of technological advance. Flaubert's 'realism' was not only an attempt to create an art that would be superior to 'disgusting' life, but also to create a truer picture than a photographer-in-prose could produce. Flaubert's successors, the naturalists, tended to believe that they could make fiction into a science, that they could improve living conditions – and that novels were documents, blueprints. But Zola, who did not even fully believe in his own theories, was more often than not a romantic decadent and a proto-surrealist (consider the death of Nana; or the emasculation of Maigrat and the sexual consummation scene in the flooded mine in *Germinal*).

IT WILL be seen, when we come to the present situation in England, why a brief, selective survey of what has gone on in Europe in the past seventy-five years is pertinent.

Although the seeds of expressionism – in its general sense, any means of revealing inner reality by external descriptions which usually seem to be, conventionally, unrealistic, non-mimetic, non-photographic – had long been sown, German Expressionism, which began in about 1910, was the first really strident modernist movement. Decadence preceded it, but the strains of practising this tended to lead to death from drink or drugs, or relieved reversion to pseudo-religion, nearly always Roman Catholic in type. Decadence has no set programme, as the Expressionists tried to have. What is most interesting about it, perhaps, is the way in which – by however crude and even vulgar means – it tried to revive that gnosticism which, though pagan in origin, had represented what might fairly be described as the rebellious 'modernism' of early Christian times. Huysmans, who of course became Catholic, describes in *La Bas* (1891) how Durtal attends a Black Mass: the account demonstrates that the object behind 'Black Magic', however hidden from the frequently stupid people who indulge in it, is to explore the gnostic belief that men are under the rule of the Devil, and that God is infinitely remote, perhaps so much so that he is inaccessible. Canon Docre, based on the real Father Louis Van Haecke, defiles the host in orgasm, and Durtal slinks away. The ancient notion, formulated in numerous ways, of the guardian angels (an import from the original Zoroastrianism – not present in its tamed, modern Parsee version) being cheats and tricksters who try to turn back the 'ascending soul', has a startling relevance to modern life, in all its over-sophisticated complexity. Its vulgarisation in the 'Magick' of Crowley – the popularity of Colin Wilson at 'lounge' level, and even above that level, is not insignificant – is paralleled by the contemporary trivialisation of modernism and by the related trampling down of the feminine, and therefore of the all-important principle of private myth-making, under the guise of acceptance of it.

The German Expressionists did have a programme, even if nothing major emerged from the exact observance of that programme (nothing that does not escape a programme ever does; but movements are needed, if only for important writers to pass through). Inspired by the graphic art of such as Van Gogh, the 'fauve' (first used in a pejorative sense, of 'wild beast', by enraged critics), Kandinsky, the now wrongly forgotten Belgian poet Verhaeren and others, they used, twisted, distorted, grotesque, usually urban imagery. They rebelled against the father, as household figure and as God; and they refused to accept the bourgeois view of reality held by their fathers and by other materialists. Very often the tight verse forms they employed gave stark emphasis to the horror of their vision, which arose from hatred of the tyranny of machinery, a sense of impending catastrophe (the war in which many of them died), and from the splintering of religious impulses: these tight forms are like little boxes containing shrieks, or give the impression of men with rigid faces and bodies twitching violently and uncontrollably. Georg Heym, as John Willett has pointed out, is a typical representative of the early phase of expressionism.

> *Your lilac waistcoat*
> *Kisses me well, you pallid painter;*
> *Chelsea-girl*
> *Your shawl shines wholly yellow;*
> *you, racket-Earl*
> *Are wearing spattered raspberry,*
> *not a tie.*

And Gottfried Benn, for a short while a supporter of Hitler, though never a Nazi (an example of the strains imposed on artists attempting to depict reality as it really is: uncomfortable, not comforting), wrote of the 'summit of creation, that swine man'.

In Italy and elsewhere F. T. Marinetti, later an extreme fascist, was propagating Futurism, for many temporary subscribers an attempt to overcome the menace of machinery by celebrating it. That celebration largely stopped after the 1914–18 war. Russian Futurism, which did not obtain its impetus from Marinetti, was also under way; its most famous figure was Mayakovsky. In Germany Expressionism had petered out by the mid-Twenties: its exponents were killed in the war, or became fascists or communists, or embraced the 'new objectivity'. But during the war certain writers and painters went to Switzerland and founded the Dada movement: this, self-consciously 'mad' and orientated towards annoying the bourgeois, organised what are today called 'happenings' (as if they were new). Only one body of work emerging from Dada – though much that came from it was delightful (some of Schwitters' poetry, for example) – was of undisputed genius: the poetry of the Alsatian sculptor Jean or Hans Arp – it is still not nearly well enough known today, and hardly any of it, to my knowledge, has been translated. Few admirers of Arp's sculpture seem to realise that he was a major poet. Dada was eventually taken over by André Breton and transformed into surrealism. This, influenced by Freud, worked from the basis that dreams and the unconscious (said to produce 'automatic writing') are truer than the products of the conscious mind, with its censoring habits. None of this happened without reason. Nor was suicide so prevalent a theme amongst the surrealists for no reason. One correctly predicted the date of his suicide ten years hence. This was his 'work'.

Long ago Bergson and William James had drawn attention to the different kinds of time, and to the nature of the stream-of-consciousness. There was 'clock-time', as Bergson acknowledged; but there was also phenomenological time, a process of becoming which rejected the false 'spatialisation' inherent in the belief that only 'clock-time' existed. Pirandello, most famous as a playwright but even better as a short-story writer, had shown that there were many types of reality, and that conventional fictions were no longer adequate to deal with modern life. South America, a country whose largely unexplored, unknown interior is an equivalent for the un-conscious mind, produced many great novelists (Onetti, Guimarães Rosa, Asturias are only examples) and great poets, including the Peruvian Vallejo, whose dislocated, powerful poetry is the greatest of the century. France 'invented' the *nouveau roman*, a sterile but philosophically important venture: a serious attempt to cope with reality. Holland pro-duced the telluric poet Gerrit Achterberg, a man who in a fit of madness had shot his wife, and who explored the themes of death and the loss of the beloved in as convincing terms as anyone of his age. Russia, before Stalin's crack-down, had more major poets than perhaps any other single country, all of them modernist. In fiction there were Zamyatin, the untamed Leonov (who still knows how to cheat, to a certain extent, the Soviet culture lackeys, with their insistence on what is no more than a totalitarian intensification of con-ventional realism: 'socialist realism') and many others; if now Solzhenitsyn tries to carry on the nineteenth-century tradition (he is not more than a highly talented novelist, and *1914* is abject), then the quieter Sinyavsky is an important and radical modernist who wrote many of his works under the very noses of the authorities until they caught up with him. Even in Franco's Spain the loyalist Vincent Aleixandre, too sick to flee the country, was able to produce a poetry truly modernist in spirit – and he has had successors. Under Salazar's Portugal Pessoa produced his best work; he was another supremely great writer, whose poetry explores, at a majestic and astonishingly lucid level, the problem of multiplicity of self. (It is only fair to add that Pessoa, a convoluted ironist and solitary drinker, did not object to Salazar's fascist regime.)

Much more could be mentioned: Proust, Gide (tester of the very validity of fiction), Romains, Dutch novelists such as Schendel, or, in our time, Boon, Austrians such as Musil and Broch, Italians such as Campana, Svevo, Quasimodo ... That is not the point of what I am writing; yet some outline has had to be made. Because members of the so-called English *avant-garde* – and now there certainly is a self-styled one – usually have little or no knowledge of European modernism (even though most of the work, especially the fiction, exists in translation); or because, with some honourable exceptions, non-creative academics have dehumanised it, absorbed it unto themselves, made it unrelatable to the act of writing in England. Two questions remain to be answered. What was happening in English writing while modernism was in its first stages (until about 1930); and what is happening now?

I should add four points. First, the recognition that some kind of change in creative procedures is necessary does not imply that all the writing of the past is therefore to be rejected (the serious Futurists, who soon rejected Marinetti, were not very serious when they said it should be: they wanted to annoy and disconcert the conformists).

Secondly, a work need not *look* modern to *be* modern – which simply means to be adequate to deal with modern reality. A good example of this is to be found in the best fiction of the shamefully neglected Norah Hoult, a story by whom appeared in the last issue of this magazine. Another example may be found in the earlier (woman) writer, the Australian Henry Handel Richardson's *The Fortunes of Richard Mahoney* (1930), a three-part masterpiece that is not even in print.

Thirdly, any kind of specific prescription is wrong: the imagination is autonomous, it does not (*pace* David Caute, who once devoted a great deal of space to attacking me on this point) and cannot obey any kind of dogma or political programme. That is called by Caute a 'mystical' view; but the accusation is merely a positivist's sly way of evading the existence of mysteries. One is not a mystic if one cannot understand the pattern of the universe, or, indeed, its absurdity, if it is absurd. One can go no further than assert that it is becoming increasingly difficult to portray reality in a conventional manner. No one minds if middlebrows discuss Iris Murdoch or Tom Stoppard, or read Nevil Shute or Melvyn Bragg; one is entitled to complain if this is called literature, rather than the entertainment – often pretentious – which it is intended to be.

Fourthly and lastly, I make special mention of a particular and early form of modernism: the *esperpento* of the Spanish novelist, poet, playwright and dramatist Ramón del Valle-Inclán. I do so because it illustrates, most appropriately, why Sinyavsky's claim is valid. It may be asserted that there is little essential in Sartre's existentialism that had not already been implied, or, often, stated, in the work of Unamuno and Ortega y Gasset. But Valle-Inclán's concept of *esperpento* (the best English translation is 'funhouse distorting mirror') is exceptionally precise. In the play *Luces de Bohemia*, of 1920, he has a character pronounce that Spain is a grotesque deformation of European civilization – and he compares this deformation to the reflection of classical heroes in the concave mirrors to be found in Madrid's amusement arcades. (There is a sensible and useful account of Valle-Inclán in G. G. Brown's *A Literary History of Spain: The Twentieth Century*,

1972). The characters of Valle-Inclán's *esperpento* 'are what they *seem to be*, or they *seem to be* what they *are*', as a critic has explained.

No further analysis of *esperpento* is required here – though English readers would do well to read Valle-Inclán. (It is significant that he is not even once mentioned in the new and large Pelican survey, *Modernism* . . .)

The point is that the situation diagnosed by Valle-Inclán, and more mildly by Unamuno before him, is now (at least) valid for everywhere. Art has something better to do, everywhere, than 'tell stories about the surface reality of contemporary life'. Except, one may add, for those who find contemporary life wholly satisfying.

THE HEYDAY of the great English realist novel virtually came to an end when Ford completed his tetralogy *Parade's End* in 1928. But even Ford was not completely English: he was partly German. Nor was Ford simply a realist. Conrad was a Pole. Henry James was American. So were Eliot and Pound.

English poetry at the turn of the century and for long afterwards was in the doldrums: Newbolt, Watson and other such versifiers were dominant. Harold Monro was active and energetic, and towards the end of his tormented life he wrote some six good poems – a far cry from the semi-Georgian verse which fills most of his posthumously *Collected Poems*. What legacy did Pound, and then Eliot, leave amongst the English poets who were influenced by them? Not much. The poems that came out of the imagist movement were certainly for the most part like little sparkling pools when compared to the escapist Georgian porridge encouraged by the well-meaning Edward Marsh. But they were slight poems; to compare imagism to expressionism or Dada or even Spanish *ultraism* is only to see more clearly how little advantage it took of the revolutionary precepts Pound put forward.

Brooke's undoubted freshness does not conceal his total lack of understanding of what was happening in the world (compare Péguy in France, or Heym or Stadler in Germany), and, even if we don't blame him for it, his famous patriotic sonnet really is specious – and even racist.

As for the war poets. Charles Sorley, who might have

become an original poet of great power, and who saw through Brooke before anyone else, was killed far too early to realise his gifts. Sassoon's genius was for bitter satire; after the war he settled down into a poet of no interest. Owen needed the war, and there is no indication that without it he would have been able to go on. Nor are his poems, except technically, more innovatory than Sassoon's: metaphors for his homosexual masochism and love of suffering, they do movingly transcend his 'case history', but they are rooted in injustice (he was, as Joseph Cohen has remarked, an 'injustice collector'). The real losses were Isaac Rosenberg and Edward Thomas. Rosenberg would have invigorated English poetry; but would his genius have been recognised? He had little but patronising attention in his short life – and what is the use of the recognition he has now, more than fifty years too late, to English poetry? As for the older Thomas: he was at his best a profounder poet than most realise, but he has never been treated (except by C. H. Sisson) as anything but a superior Georgian – and he, too, was unknown in his lifetime.

That part of the English poetry-reading public which did not devote itself to escapist verse – oddly enough, a large proportion of immediately contemporary verse is neo-Georgian – regarded Auden, Day-Lewis, Spender, Mac-Neice, Dylan Thomas and George Barker as 'modern'. Ironically, they got better poetry, on the whole, from the poets they regarded as 'old-fashioned': from Edward Thomas, W. H. Davies, Andrew Young (the two latter were not modernists, but wrote in a formal poetic tradition at a time when it was just still possible to do so). Walter de la Mare, when he was not being intolerably 'poetical' (which he often was), was a sinister and decadent expressionist, a true modernist, both in poetry and fiction, who certainly saw things in a 'distorting mirror', and who saw them true. Ironically, he would have denied this: he had no notion of his modernity, nor has any critic (besides Geoffrey Grigson and myself) ever seen him as essentially a modernist.

What of Auden, Day-Lewis, Spender and MacNeice? Auden began as an authentic poet inasmuch as he was excited by words. But his metrical – rather than rhythmical – facility did not disguise the adolescent ill-accomplishment of his early expressionism – as the recent issue of his complete poems amply demonstrates. He soon petered out into a lazy and disingenuous bore, evading the problems of his homosexuality, of which he was ashamed. Day-Lewis was a neo-Georgian pasticheur. Spender was a literary egg-bound fowl: his earliest poems have great appeal, and were more resolved than Auden's. But he never became the figure he might have been. MacNeice was unable to express his terrible and authentic sense of distress, which comes over, muted, as the modulated sensitivity of a literary butterfly. In the end he took to violent drinking bouts (as a result of which he died prematurely) as a substitute for poetry. Dylan Thomas produced a Swinburnian magma influenced by T. F. Powys, Joyce, the Bible and a dash of surrealism – but few of his poems mean anything in expressionist terms; rather their incoherence hides an exceptionally formalist approach. All that can be claimed for him was that he had nerve. Barker, a superior though wildly uneven poet, has never had his due; yet at his best he was anticipating the genuine modernism of Berryman and many others in the Thirties. The point here is that he never *has* had his due; what he achieved has seldom been seen as modern. *Calami-terror* risks being ridiculous, and often is; but it is as near to surrealism as anything published in England in the Thirties. It does not achieve the status of *personal* and coherent myth which a truly modernist writing in English, with its unavoidably empirical elements, demands; but it reaches out for it. And it is imbued with a distinct and authentic sense of male guilt. The poetry of the Forties, much of it produced by the self-styled 'new Apocalyptics', was either unintentionally comic pastiche of American and European poetry (for example of Stevens and Éluard) or it drew too mechanically on established myth (Treece, Watkins). One could make a better case for Empson and Graves. But surely it is significant that Empson had more or less stopped writing poetry by the end of the war – I saw him greeted with silence at a big London poetry-reading in about 1942, whereas Day-Lewis was rapturously applauded – and that Graves has not a drop of English blood in his veins? Graves, anyway, is what Empson himself would call, as he calls Hart Crane, a 'special case', needing a special approach. Essentially a modernist (read 'The Terraced Valley'), he has not helped himself by denouncing 'continental influences'; and he was in any case virtually ignored as a poet until his 'discovery' in America in the late Fifties. In England it is, generally, his late, lapidary poems that get the attention – not the ones he wrote in the Thirties and early Forties.

Surrealism may have its silly side, and it (like 'structuralist poetics') certainly 'works' less well in English than in French. But it needed adaptation – and it hardly got it. Roditi, who, although educated in England, is not English, published his first book in France. And who has now heard of Roger Roughton (who gassed himself in a Dublin flat in the Thirties) or the charming surrealist poems of Francis Scarfe, now an understandably somewhat soured academic who took to a formal manner of poetry writing after the war, before he gave it up altogether? The precocious quasi-surrealist poems of David Gascoyne now read very much like pastiche of Éluard and others; 'Salvador Dali', properly recognised as at least worthy of note by Michael Roberts in his *Faber Book of Modern Verse*, is merely a description of a Dali-type canvas – but Dali, amusing though some of his exploits have been, was a mere exploiter of surrealism – not one of his pictures is better than Hunt's 'The Scapegoat', and not one makes a real technical advance on it. Dali is to surrealism what the Beatles were to Varese . . . Gascoyne anyway became a nervous Christian, who often spoiled his poems by the use of over-long lines, and who has long ago relapsed into (at least apparent) silence.

The English, with a few exceptions such as Eliot, were not kind to Joyce – who does not come into this story because he was Irish (he considered Ireland an 'afterthought of Europe' and never even took England seriously). The critics, however, were kind to Dorothy M. Richardson. They claimed that she was the chief English exponent of stream-of-consciousness. No error could be more revealing.

The English are not generally aware that there are two sorts of stream-of-consciousness, only one of which is authentic. The important sort is expressionist: it uses images, or other imaginative devices, to express inner processes, or even the inner reality of situations. It is the artistic substitute for (scientifically) psychological investigation of mental process; and it has revealed more. Pseudo-stream-of-consciousness is merely an attempt to extend conventional realism; it is seen at its most extreme in Holz's and Schlaf's comparatively early 'Sekundenstil' style, which tried to reproduce the passing of seconds and failed just because it ignored what Bergson and James were to point out: that phenomenological times does not work like clock-time, that mental processes are not at all understood, that the mind does not consist only of consciousness. Richardson practised the second kind of method, and her novels are as dull as her heroine is boring. She is not in any sense a pioneer.

Lastly: if Virginia Woolf is hurled at me as a pioneer who was recognised as a pioneer in her own country I can only suggest that my readers test the quality of the English criticism of her work, which is in any case frequently disfigured by extraordinarily conventional 'purple passages', and is not what it seems.

I WROTE in 1973 that the notion of London's being regarded as in any sense a centre of cultural or literary activity was no more than a bad joke, for which I was taken to task by London-based poeticules. Once, before the 1914–18 war, it could have been so called. Yet nearly all the major figures were not English. Only Wyndham Lewis (and even he was born off the Newfoundland coast) could claim to be a real Englishman. And what has been his fate? First, ostracism. Then, long after his death in 1956, a rehabilitation. But what kind of rehabilitation? In almost every case, a dull attempt to relate him to an academic tradition to which he does not belong – the worst example of this is the abysmal short study by W. H. Pritchard – but Pritchard is, one must admit, an American. Of Englishmen only Grigson has written decently of his literary achievement – and then in a long out-of-print pamphlet. Lewis attracted much of the odium heaped upon him by his journalistic laziness and tactless baiting of the orthodox left, who may have been foolish but had, sometimes, concern. But he was punished primarily because his prose seemed 'unreal'; he regarded the 'herd', in his own memorable phrase, as 'hallucinated automata'. His last great work, *The Human Age* – unhappily unfinished – may be claimed as the most phantasmagoric piece of fiction published in the past fifty years. And yet compare the attention it has received to that given to the novels of Iris Murdoch or, at a lower level, Margaret Drabble, who practises a candidly conventional realism: her novels give the impression of propaganda films put out by an organisation that might call itself Modified Women's Liberation.

Lewis makes no attempt to hold a mirror up to nature, to imitate external reality. His prose, as Grigson once put it, is 'mineral'. Its complex dialectic is undoubtedly gnostic in spirit (Lewis's own sporadic explanations of it hardly do it justice – for the intellect alone can never do justice to the imagination).

Why should this work be more or less ignored by reviewers and academics alike, when that of far inferior writers is widely discussed? And who if anyone has approached its level?

Anyone who has seen a novel by Irish Murdoch will note, collected on the jacket, dozens of superlatives. Some of these are merely the phrases of tired, inadequately read reviewers – 'better and better' and so on, the stock-in-trade of such hacks as Auberon Waugh when he is feeling well and free from envy – but others come from critics regarded as distinguished. But of what does Miss Murdoch's profuse fiction consist? Properly examined, it reveals itself as an inorganic patch-work of bathetic dialogue, sentimental portraits of 'virtuous' characters, pet- and weather-notes, embarrassing descriptions of sexual encounters – all written in an unexcited prose around plots which draw on every kind of fashionably sensationalist theme: homosexuality, incest, murder, you name it. It is failed neo-baroque, without imaginative energy. And the appraisal of it is readily seen to be artificial. Here is a writer intelligent enough to try to avoid conventional realism, but who succeeds only in covering up her inadequacy by resort to gimmick. The result is jerky and grotesque in the wrong sense. And, curiously, she reminds one of the Forties poets when she makes use, mechanically and self-consciously, of myth.

The present is, to put it mildly, an improbable one. The majority of non-academic reviewers are as they have always been: men and women more worried about what they *ought* to say than to record their own response. Soon they get into the habit of not responding at all. Those who seem different are usually trading on the shock that their eccentricity will produce: what harm has Kingsley Amis (not, admittedly, primarily a reviewer) done himself by saying that Spillane is better than Hammett or that John D. MacDonald is 'by any standards a better writer than Saul Bellow'? Such reviewers want to get on; and they like the scene they see outside their windows when they get up in the morning – it is 'just like life'.

The academics have of course more knowledge. But with honourable exceptions, they contribute to the climate of warm indifference. There are several techniques by which the academic can revenge himself for his non-creativity (one of the worst is to write 'novels', which need not here be discussed). First, he can wrap up his knowledge so that it remains inaccessible. Secondly, he can beat his readers over the head with ultra-specialised knowledge. George Steiner, who is intelligent, cannot resist practising a combination of these two methods – which helps to conceal the empty rhetoric he employs as a substitute for his creative sterility. Thirdly, and most commonly, he can demonstrate his lack of engagement with his subject; he may even, like Henri Peyre, call himself 'we' and maintain a lofty detachment from literature altogether; but this is relatively rare in England.

Why this monstrous take-over bid by criticism from creativity? Why this lack of attention to the few real innovators in the interests of middlebrow novelists who will, in a few years, be regarded as Charles Morgan or A. S. M. Hutchinson are now (hardly at all). The reasons are complicated. Certainly in France, Italy and Germany criticism *tries* to be superior to creative art – sometimes comically so. But creative art continues. France has Simon, Italy Cassola, Germany Grass (these are examples). But England does not have authors of this calibre under seventy – or nothing like as many.

The English empirical tradition has much to do with it. An English writer needs to create an extra dimension of coherence if he wants to communicate – and communication is one of the reasons for writing. And then possibly some of the Dutch or French or Germans are just as dissatisfied with their situation as some of us are with ours. But would, elsewhere, such a successfully nightmarish novel as Ballard's *Crash* have been dealt with in other countries as it was here? It may or may not have been a financial success. That is not the point. Its critical fate was to be judged from the standpoint of SF; and many people felt that it was a fantasy and that, while 'gripping', the author should 'see a psychiatrist'. SF is now sometimes called 'speculative fiction'. But all fiction must now be 'speculative', in one way or another. This is no longer a special and inferior category. Who – if indeed there were more than a few dozen competent psychiatrists about – does *not* need to see a psychiatrist? Ballard's book is *not* a 'fantasy'. It is (broadly speaking) an expressionist novel describing the *real*, the inner, state of a certain important aspect of modern life. One could simply describe motorways, the desire of men for Elizabeth Taylor, sexual case-histories, plastic surgery, fast driving, the car-as-penis. It has been done. But Ballard combines all this into a hallucinated vision, full of meaningful phenomenological detail. *Crash* may not be a great novel. But it is truly modern. It is worth more than any number of documentaries on the subjects it deals with. And so consider the evasive tactics of its readers: 'I am compelled by this, but of course it's unhealthy and it's only a science thriller . . .' In fact it gives a truer picture of life not only than that given by the media but also than that given by 'scientific' or 'sociological' analysis. *Crash* could hardly be ignored, even if its power can be conveniently diverted by describing it as 'abnormal' or 'fantasy'. A few other books are less fortunate in that they are ignored altogether.

Let independent and heretical readers, then, ignore the supposed authority of the 'critics' (or most of them). Horror is not the only way into the kind of expanded reality which modernism seeks. Sinyavsky (again) has spoken of 'comic inventiveness as a means of bringing home the deadly earnest'. The *avant-garde* had almost exhausted itself in Europe by 1930, although the catastrophes of 1939–45 saw some resurgence of it. It did catch up in England, but in trivialised and commercialised forms: the zaniness of pop groups or, more amusingly, in such as *The Goon Show* or *Monty Python*. It is up to us to wrest it from the hands of commerce, of the novelists and reviewers who parrot its outside appearance and by doing so deny its inside nature, and of the literary historians. We cannot and should not be other than English (which we have to accept whether we like it or not); but we can begin by looking at European modernism through our own eyes, and considering how its techniques might be applied to our own literature. Imagination and laughter may well step in at this point.

JULIAN ROTHENSTEIN

EMMA TENNANT

Philomela

BEFORE I married, when we lived in Athens, the bright emptiness of the long days was made bearable by my sister Philomela, who spoke the thoughts I hardly knew I had.

Why permit yourself to be taken off like a slave? We can leave Athens and go and live in the mountains. We will be free. And if we die, anything better than the life that lies ahead of us.

I knew she was right, but I couldn't find the courage to go. The nights are cold in the mountains, and we would almost certainly perish. Tereus came and married me and we went to Thrace in a procession of such magnificence that I knew I would never come back. When my son Itylus was born, I felt as if I had been buried in a soft tomb.

I'll come and live with you, Philomela said. You won't have to wait long.

She never came. I moped, like the birds my children bring back when they go out for a walk. Tereus noticed, but he didn't care. The palace, as it is now, was always full of young men singing, and preparations for war, and the bustle of sandalled feet going aimlessly back and forth on the worn marble. I stayed on my couch, almost pleased that my beauty was going and that I was unable to sleep at night. It was a slow death, but no one who is buried alive dies quickly.

Then one day Tereus said he would go and find my sister. There had been no wars for two years, and the festivities were palling. He was looking older himself; perhaps only bloodshed kept him young; at any rate he wanted to travel, and he liked the idea of doing something gallant and slightly ridiculous. To his delight, everyone laughed when he said he was going to rescue my sister from her monotonous life in Athens.

It was at the height of summer that he set off. When he had gone I went down into the gardens for the first time for years and looked in an interested way at the flowers and the strolling peacocks. My children even smiled at me when I went up to them. I pretended to myself that my health had changed, that I had been ill for a long time and was now quite naturally better, but I knew that it was really because Philomela was coming that I saw these things in a different way. Her face and her voice kept flowing through me as I paced out the rest of the day, glancing foolishly at the position of the sun in the sky. It was a long journey, and it might be weeks before Tereus brought her back.

Tereus came back one winter day. The air was clear and I could see a huddle of people galloping across the plain. My throat ached, as if I had tried to shout to them across that distance, and my hands kept flying to my neck and pulling at the gold chains I wore. Then I felt I was going to cry, and I sent for Coda to bring me a herb drink that soothes my mind. I even thought for a moment of climbing to the temple. But I restrained myself, in case Philomela should climb the wide steps when I wasn't there to see her. And I wanted to show her the garden we had made, to take her into the house of which I felt suddenly proud.

Tereus' head seemed larger, I remember that. And the young men with him hung back, which they don't usually do – no one ran past me with a quick salute on the way to the courtyard and the refreshing wine. Tereus' head loomed over me like a round polished shield. His tongue moved thickly in his dry lips.

Philomela is dead, he said.

I spent a year in that room. When the sun lurked in the courtyard, beyond the hangings, which it did in the morning early when the slaves were washing the stone-fruited floors, I lifted my goblet of wine and poured it down my throat. All day long I called for more wine – and Coda and Dita brought it with lowered eyes.

I gave birth to another child. Itylus came and sat with me sometimes, but he was learning to go out with his father more. He had a horse of his own. When I asked him about the garden we had made, he was embarrassed and changed the subject. I began to suspect that it was overgrown, or that Tereus had got rid of it altogether. Not that I really cared. The garden had been for Philomela, and she would never come now.

When the new child was beginning to learn how to crawl about on the soft rugs in my room, I got up for the first time and went onto the wide porch that looks over the plain. It was summer, and birds were singing in the thicket of olives. My eyes were tired from crying: they had changed their shape now and slanted down in the corners instead of being round.

I gazed out at all the empty expanses around me. Sky.

Earth. Distant mountain. None of them contained anything at all.

I leant back against a pillar and sighed. My back was weak after so long in my room. A slave came up the steps towards me. He stopped, surprised to see me there, and then prostrated himself.

He had something for me: it seemed to be a bundle of cloth. I took it listlessly – a present no doubt from one of the noble women I no longer consented to see. The slave glanced anxiously at me once, and then ran into the house. I opened the bundle, yawning.

A tapestry. My eyes were blurred, and I had to bring it up close to my face to see what scenes were depicted. Chariots in Thrace, I thought at first, and noble warriors under a spiky sun. Then I saw that the chief figure was Tereus himself.

This is amusing, I said aloud. Is Tereus worth this? I looked closer.

In the first scene, Tereus was embracing a woman passionately. Her face was obscured; I smiled. In the second, I saw it. The owner of the face was cringing at Tereus' feet and she was pleading for mercy. Philomela. In the next scene he had advanced on her. He cut out her tongue. In the following scene Philomela, imprisoned in a castle, looked out as Tereus galloped away into the distance. That was all. I looked again. There was no doubt about it. Philomela.

I went to my room and sat holding the tapestry. Tereus' feet sounded in the courtyard outside: I pushed the tapestry under the couch and sat there as I had for so long, doing nothing. But he didn't come in.

So I was able to form my plan. I sent for Coda and Dita. I told them my suspicions and I gave the last of my gold for the search. Somewhere, between here and Athens, Philomela suffered alone. Secretly, men were found and set out on their horses. It was late at night when they left, and my heart beat loudly as I listened to the hooves growing fainter on the plain.

They found her and brought her back. Poor, dumb Philomela. And we all feasted, the smoke from the burning flesh of the animals went up into the sky for hours before we ate, the fountain was fed with wine, Tereus kept laughing and saying he must have made a mistake. He was so frightened he couldn't even find an excuse. So we ate and drank, and the wild boars on our gold cups chased themselves endlessly round as the gold glinted in the light from the torches and the round heads of Tereus' friends shone the same bright colour. Philomela never once looked reproach.

We lay together in my room, and I whispered in her ear. Her eyes could always answer me. And we knew we would avenge ourselves on Tereus.

Philomela lay in the prow of the boat. Her black hair just touched the water. I watched her all the time – for signs of happiness, or discontent, or simply to see what her eyes would say to me. Today she was smiling, and we glided at the rhythm of her breathing over water so clear that the smallest pebbles on the bottom looked as big and white as rocks.

We were there because a war was raging inland. On the shore, brightly coloured as victory, were Tereus' tents. From the beach little wisps of black smoke went up: the slaves were preparing the evening meal.

Tereus comes back from the war tonight. His fingers will pull at roasted meat. His mouth will be red with juice. The singing will start in a dull roar, and torches will be lit on the sand. Dancing figures, giants inside the tents but small in the great expanse outside, will run from every angle to the edge of the sea. Because of the wine, the moon will shine brilliantly.

The four curved paddles of our boat guided us gently back to land. I stepped out, with Philomela in my arms, and set her down on the stones. We both stood for a moment, looking at the tents and the blade of blue which carves out the clumsy shapes of the mountains; but we saw only the evening ahead. It was months since Tereus had gone to the war. We had almost forgotten his face. He had gone, probably, because the embarrassment was too great for him at home – and he hoped, while he was away, that we would forget what he had done. We thought of him as we walked up to the encampment. And without glancing at each other again, we went to lie down until the heat of the day had passed.

The sun lay to one side of the sky and our shadows were long when we left the great tent and went inland to the olive groves. The preparations for the banquet were growing more frantic – and it was only when we were surrounded by bushes of myrtle and thyme that we were able to go on without vomiting on the ground. The smell of burning meat was so strong.

Philomela saw Itylus first. I followed the line of her pointing finger and could just make out, in the gloom where the trees were thicker, a group of boys playing at war. Itylus had a bow and arrow, and was running importantly from tree to tree calling out commands. As Tereus' son he was obeyed: this had made him arrogant, but charming still; already he had taken on the pompous, exaggerated stride of his father.

Now he sent a shower of arrows over our heads and the other boys ran laughing towards us to retrieve them. They all liked Philomela, and made a pretence of searching in the glade at her feet so she could stroke them and smile. And she did! While my heart beat heavily and slowly, and my legs felt as rooted and shapeless as the lines of trees that marched out to all sides of us.

Itylus!

I had to call him, of course – but if only it could have been Philomela! What do you want?

Anything to have been spared the sound of his voice. As I made no sign of moving, he came reluctantly forward. He knew I had come to spoil his game. It's nearly dark, I said. Your father is coming. We must go back to the tents.

He shrugged, then followed. We went in single file down to the beach.

Tereus will come down the mountain pass as the sun is setting. Taking advantage of the glory; wearing the flaming sky like a cloak he has picked up on the battlefield. Boasting as he tramps through the encampment. Flinging himself down, the exhausted warrior, and waiting for us, my tongue-less sister and his wife to shower our praise on him.

On the pretext of showing him a big sea animal that had been caught in the nets that morning, we took Itylus into the cave at the other end of the beach. It was dark there, with a rancid smell: the colour of the air was the same deep grey all the way up to the roof of the cave and the rocks were thin and sharp like the teeth of a rotting fish. The children made piles of the fragile sea anemones and we crunched them under foot as we walked, the shells the faint pink-blue of an earlobe. Philomela and I stood silently by as Itylus, with controlled excitement, examined the monster.

A great eye lay in a network of tentacles. The confused limbs, sprawled now on the stale sand at the back of the cave, had evidently put up a fight – here and there they had been hacked by mens' hands and were crushed like a reed that someone has tried to break off and then abandoned. Perhaps because of the eye, which seemed, wherever we stood, to be watching us, we were afraid to go too near. Only Itylus, to show his courage and manhood, picked up a piece of drift-wood and advanced on it cautiously. It was dead since morning; but the glare of the black pupil in the pool of white suggested hidden power and energy. In our minds, we saw it rise and attack. The limbs, although twisted and battered, had a febrile strength. We felt them crush our ribs and wind themselves round our necks.

We lifted a boulder and came up on Itylus from behind. He fell without a sound. Philomela's eyes spoke terror. I was the only one to cry out.

The sound I made was flung back by the walls of the cave in anger and contempt. It took a long time to die, lingering in a whimper in the wet stone.

The eye still watched us as we lifted the body of Itylus and crept to the mouth of the cave with it. I looked out first. The sun was setting, the sky was red. I could see nothing of the black mountains, but a contingent of men, torches lit in preparation for the sudden descent of night, were moving like fiery beetles from the beach to the foothills. Tereus must be on his way down, then.

How quick and how slow our dragging of the great pot from its hiding place in the entrance of the cave, our pyre of dry wood, the heating of the water. But when we looked out at the sea, we saw his floating hair. And the sand in the red glow from the sinking sun was the colour of his poor boiling flesh. How slow!

Years and years will pass, and these minutes will still be longer than them all. Every hour will be made up out of them. And we will be standing by the staring eye in the back of the cave and Tereus will be coming down the hill and we will be standing at the mouth of the cave and looking out at the sea to shift the time. How quickly the years will pass!

When the meat was ready we drained the water away until there was only a little at the bottom of the pot. We had tried to find fresh water – there was an old well just above the beach – but seawater had seeped in. Tiny limpets and shreds of sour weed clung to the flesh. We threw in herbs and animal fat. Philomela made a dough with her agile fingers, which she used for speaking now, holding them up and flashing combinations of numbers when she had to make it clear what she wanted. I watched her hands as she laid the fine crust over the pot. We built up the fire, and waited.

It was a fine banquet. I sat at Tereus' side, my eyes down, my face flushed with pride for him. Philomela, as always on these occasions, was a ghost, a shadow that fell only occasionally across his face if he should look round and see her. I was his wife; and I celebrated his victories with him.

The men shouted and sang. When the moon rose, some of them ran drunkenly to the entrance to the tent, and gazed up at it as if it had appeared for the first time. Like Tereus, I laughed indulgently at them. Like Tereus, I applauded when the captive slave girls danced, their bodies greased and jewels shining between their eyes. With Tereus I rose and walked to the great table where the wine and food was laid out. On the glistening fig leaves, grapes and pomegranates stood in mounds. Great sides of roasted ox were garlanded with fast-wilting flowers.

The pie was brought in. Tereus sat down like a child and ate. When he had eaten a few mouthfuls, he nodded his approval. He offered some to his favourites, and they swaggered forward, holding out their hands. Then he turned to me.

Eat! – he said. You have done well.

I shook my head. Black, dizzy sickness. Inside me an ill-tempered sea rolled violently. I had to look up. Eyes looked back at me with a mixture of curiousity and dislike. Where is Philomela?

But her eyes had gone. And I half fell, as all the eyes there in that room merged together and one eye, lidless, staring shone out at me. Tereus, the juice from the pie dribbing down his chin, pulled me back on the seat beside him with astonishment. He thrust a tender morsel in my face. Eat! he said laughing. What's the matter with you?

Philomela came forward from the back of the tent. Because she was dumb the men were afraid of her, and they fell back easily enough to let her through. I felt Tereus wince.

Take that woman away! he muttered. But his voice lacked conviction: like the others, he was afraid of her. She had become, in the camp, like the priestess of an oracle without a voice. She was the unconscious avenger of every sin. If only Tereus knew the barbarity she had suffered, the others guessed at it.

She reached my side and took my hand so I could rise with new strength. Except for distant shouting outside, her silence had spread. The eyes looked at us now with fear and unease. They were waiting: waiting for me to speak.

I turned to Tereus.

It is for you to eat your son Itylus, I said. You destroyed us long ago.

(How slow! Tereus' long years of exile and grief. How quickly the years will pass.)

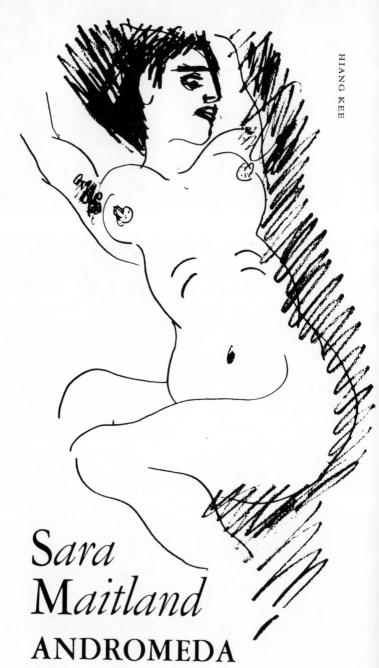

Sara
Maitland
ANDROMEDA

112

MY MOTHER would say that it was wrong to call one's husband a thief, Mine is. Thief, thief, thief, I scream at him silently.

My mother would say that it was worse than wrong to hate one's husband, to stay awake through the night and pray for his death. I do. Die, die. I curse him while he sleeps.

My mother would say it was the worst crime to loath one's children and wish they had never been born. I do that too.

My mother was a great queen, a beautiful woman and a loving mother. She fed me at her own royal breast until I was over five years old. I can remember the sweet whiteness and warmth of her cradling me. Like a queen bee in a hive I was fed on royal jelly. I slept in her bed with her until I was nearly grown-up. If I woke in the night she would stroke me and sooth me back into gentle dreams, holding me close against her own softness.

My father was a king, a true hero; he sailed with the Argonauts on the last great adventure of the golden age. He was away for most of my childhood, but he was always devoted to my mother and me.
My husband is a thief, a bastard and a patricide.

Perseus the golden, son of Zeus, the slayer of the Gorgon, the saviour of Andromeda, the founder of Mycenae. Ha.

They don't know I'm mad. No one knows I'm mad. It's my own secret. I guard it closer than I guard my life. It's mine, mine, the only thing of my own that he has left me. I will die before I let him take that too. My madness and my hatred: fed on the milk I would not feed my children, nursed on the breast where I would not nurse my sons.

Perseus' queen walks gently through the court, a model wife, calm but busy, her eyes lowered, veiled by her long dark lashes, an example to all young women in her modesty, her humility, the love and duty that she shows her husband. She seldom raises her eyes except to smile benignly on her husband's subjects or sweetly, gratefully at him.

But Andromeda is mad, mad, mad, and no one knows. In the night she roams the palace, nursing the famous dagger with which her husband killed the Gorgon, planning her thrusts, in and out, in and out; blows of vengeance that would make her more famous even than he is. He claims Pallas Athena gave him her helmet to make him invisible. I need no helmet; no one is more invisible than his good, gentle, devoted wife. That is more than helmet, it is a whole armour of invisibility, which the mad woman wears all day and is safe. Mercifully he is also a fool. There are days when I sit beside him at the table, eating my meal and watching him through my meek, humble eyes, watching him shovel his food between his thick red lips, watching his coarse mouth masticate and his throat heave as he swallows it down, and wishing that each mouthful was snake's venom. And I think, How can he be so stupid? How can he not feel the waves of poison pour out of me and into his food, thrusting down and into his innards, as he has thrust his poison into mine? And then he will turn to me and say in his silly sickly smiling voice, 'My Andromeda, aren't you hungry? Don't you like this food? You eat like a bird, my little chicken.' And he may pick up some revolting morsel and try to feed me with his own sweaty, blood-stained hands.

When I was a child I sat on the laps of my mother's Eunuchs and they would feed me sweets and peaches, their soft rounded fingers caressing my hair, and I would hop like a humming bird from silky nest to silky nest, or come to rest against my mother's naked arms and she would reach for a grape for me; or I would bury my face in her warm sweet-smelling stomach and taste the softness of her for a dark moment.

He bangs and crashes, leaping up from the table, calling for more wine, shouting at his friends, bantering crudely, challenging someone to some absurd contest, stripping off his tunic, yelling for his horse, his slave, his hounds, his spear. Pausing only to stroke the golden hairs on his chest with a little tender gesture, he dashes outside and for hours I have to hear the wild shouts and confused arguing from the gymnasium or the arena. Then he comes puffing in again, victorious, performing to me, crying out, 'Admire Me

Admire Me.' It is not an appeal, it is an expression of his conviction that I, and everyone else in the world must share his admiration of himself. He believes I admire him, because he completely believes he is admirable. He notices nothing; not even the fact that his subjects and so called friends always let him win every game, being sensible men and as aware as I am which way survival lies; and certainly not that the golden hairs he strokes are fading and yellowish, or that the famous manly chest is slipping slower lower. Yes, he's a fool my husband as well as a thief.

But sometimes I do envy him his perfect unshakeable arrogance and blindness. He can see everything exactly as he wants it to be. His loving devoted wife. His fine sons, his chaste daughter. His enthusiastic subjects. And above all his heroic, wonderful self. I tell you seriously, he sincerely believes he is the son of Zeus. His mother's family were very strict, and she was kept permanently under guard to keep her chaste. It didn't work, she became pregnant from 'a shower of gold' as popular idiom has it. The only thing anyone knows about my husband's father is that he was rich enough to bribe the guards. But Perseus has chosen from childhood to believe it literally. His mother was imprisoned, but beloved of the Gods and Zeus disguised himself as a shower of gold in order to impregnate her. We got on rather well his mother and I; we shared something in common, we had both been driven mad by him – she through devotion and I through hatred – mad to the point that we could see through him. We never spoke of it, but just occasionally we would exchange tiny glances of amusement, of complicity, from beneath our chastely lowered lashes.

We all have to hear the story of his birth even more frequently since, in a fit of showing off at some public games, he managed to kill off his grandfather. Now of course he was fated by destiny from the beginning of time to do this. That is why his mother was in the tower, that is why, under the influence of predetermined Fate, Zeus had to be his father. Or, in more simple words, like everything else that goes wrong in his life: It Wasn't His Fault. Because he is perfect.

Sometimes I really cannot believe that a grown man can

accept this self-created delusion as an historical fact, but if you start from an unassailable assumption that you are perfect anything and everything becomes perfectly logical. The great advantage of being a King is that you can deal very effectively with anyone who is foolish enough to express a contrary opinion. Which is one of the reasons why I keep quiet. I am going to live to see him dead. With my own wifely hands I shall perform my ritual office. I am disgusted, I say publicly, by those queens who hire professional substitutes. 'How brave, how devoted, how good our queen is,' they murmur. With my own hands I am going to wipe that smug smile off his face, gently and with such joy I am going to close those pretty blue eyes, and then when he is no longer watching me, I shall spit in his face and laugh. I shall wear the full, heavy, royal mourning veil when we process to his mausoleum; I shall wear it so that no one will see the unholy glee on my face when they seal up that body for the worms to devour. Yes, yes, I shall long to see you then, Perseus the golden, the favourite of the Gods, with the worms boring and thrusting down into your bloated flesh and growing fat on your decay. They are on my side, King of Mycenae. Everything you have stolen from me they will steal back again, strip away the layers of beauty and complacency, and expose what I have known from the very beginning, the stinking putrifying foulness of your inner being, my dear husband, my own sweet royal lord. You thief, you fat arrogant hog of a petty thief. They hang men like you daily in the courtyard and I lean out the window, secretly, and imagine it is you, rotting, with the birds picking out your eyes. I laugh and laugh, mighty slayer of the Gorgon, to think how little those snaky tresses will help you then.

When I was a child they called me their little bird, as I pecked and chirped and sang through the palace. I long and desire to chirp as I peck at your dead eyes, and sing as the worms destroy your proud manhood.

His pride is at the root of him. He is that and nothing more. It is easy to understand; yes I can be understanding too, I can say how hard it must be to be a landless child, a fatherless son at the mercy of a whim of charity from foreigners, cast away unwanted and unrecognised by his own family.

I can understand what that lack would do to a pretty, able child and to a passionate headstrong adolescent. I can understand how the lust to say 'Mine', to own to possess to lay claim to everything would grow in a person from that background. Understand yes. Forgive, tolerate, even care. No. No, because it is not right, but no even more because I am one of the things possessed, taken over, made into his. His, His, Everything has to be His. 'It was love at first sight.' He says of me. 'As soon as I saw her I knew that I would run any risk, dare any venture, if I could make her my own. Don't believe anyone who says there is no such thing as Love at first sight. We know better don't we, my own?'

Love at first sight. It was jealousy at first sight. He was passing through Ethiopia and found that someone else was the hero of the moment. That was the intolerable thing, that someone else, not him, had laid claim to a moment of history. That he could not endure. If love was the price of grabbing one more chance of being the great hero he was more than willing to pay it. But for me it was my moment. The moment that I chose, that I had dedicated to myself; my one chance, the one time when I had a choice and could offer myself, as some thing more than the little princess, their bird, their darling; I was to be the pure, the chosen symbol of my mother's love for her people. The only acceptable sacrifice, the only freely offered gift. Can you understand? When the sea monster raged up from the deep, my happy homeland was turned overnight into a place of despair. And only I could save them. I offered myself as a sacrifice for my city. The perfect sacrifice has to be offered voluntarily. I offered. What were my motives? Love I say, my one true impulse of love. Perhaps there were other things in it too; things that were less pure, dark poisoned things. But it was my decision for my life; my own moment of choice and I chose it. The mixture of joy and grief that greeted my offer confirmed me. They all needed me in a way that is very rarely offered to women.

How can I describe it? There was an hysteria in me and in the whole city for the week of the ritual purification. Was it here that the seeds of my madness were sown? I know that is possible, but if things had fallen out as they were meant to, what would my madness or sanity have mattered. The rituals are complex and, to the uninitiate, uninteresting – the important factor is the growing separateness of the chosen person. I had to move from the palace to a special appointed room inside the temple; the day before the last day my mother came to say good-bye to me, she was the last person allowed to do so, I had not seen my father since the second day, after this farewell she would not be allowed to touch me or even speak to me. I lay in her arms, neither of us weeping, just close and tender. She petted me, kissed and embraced me. Her last words were, 'My sweetheart, I'm heart broken, but for myself, not for you. I almost envy you, I'm glad, I love you so much, I could never have borne losing you. I always wanted this, to be able to keep you pure and safe, and free from so much. And now you'll never have to know. O treasure, sweet heart. A bride of the sea, the sweet clean gentle sea. O my beloved. Be strong.' For the last time I buried myself in her softness, the two of us twined together, our lips against each other. But when she went I felt only a growing excitement and certainty.

In the morning the priestesses came to dress me. The soft white dress felt like my mother's last caress, but the scent of the flowers was almost overwhelming, sweet and cloying; a marked contrast to the bitter rich smell of the incense which was now burning everywhere. My head began to swim and my stomach contract in nervous, thrilling spasms. The hands of the priestesses seemed to dance over my body. I wanted to rush into the sea now, to have it round me, embracing me, cool but strong. We set in slow procession for the half-mile to the shore. The jewel green, sheep-cropped sea grass seemed as buoyant as waves, and the sea daisies almost blindingly white. The sun warmed the back of my neck as it rose over the city and through the thin white robe I could feel the breeze with my whole body. Where the grass comes to an end and the firm sand beach begins we stopped. About fifty yards away, where the water begins, there is a jagged outcrop of rock, on the seaward side of which I would wait, invisible from the land, totally exposed to the sea. The priestess bent down and cut my sandal thongs so that I could step out of them. I raised my arms and cried my intention to the sea, that I came freely to be given to the sea by my people, in love and in duty. Then the priestess cut the bands that held my hair, and the back of my neck felt suddenly cool where it was protected from the sun. Again I called out that without ties and freely I offered myself to the sea. Then finally the priestess cut through the girdle of my dress and it fell gently down my body. I stepped out of it and naked began to walk along the marked path to the rock. The solemn Lament for the Maiden began and to its beautiful notes I walked round the rock and out of life.

The waves lapped my feet and the sea was very bright. I remember quite clearly hearing the sound of the lament, feeling the wine cool dampness of the rock behind me and enjoying a moment of contentment and joyous expectation. Then the sun seemed to quiver, followed by a moment of unnatural stillness, and four huge waves lashed out at me, beating me down onto the rock, the hot strong waves of the monster's breath; I fought to receive the full impact of them, embracing their thrust and feeling them soak right into me; I caught a sort of glance, hardly that, a physical sensation of the golden lion who hunts with his mane as the waves, I don't know, don't remember, can't describe. I leaned longingly towards that hot mouth that would finish all things with its welcome. And sweaty and muscle-bound He ripped me from my triumph.

With the help of that serpented prophanity of his he stole my moment and made it his. I didn't know at once what had happened, but I did know heart-breakingly that something had gone absolutely and forever wrong. He could not allow anyone else so much as a single instant of courage or gener-osity, He stole it, he stole my moment, robbed me of my own choice, violated my sacrifice. He stole the one thing I had; stole it and possessed it and made it his own.

What else he and his snake friend stole from me I do not like to think of.

Well, in the eyes of the world, I have been a good wife to him. I never saw that I had any choice; he stole my moment from me and I was never granted another. But my husband is a thief and in those depths of me which even he can never ravage, I revile him.

'SYLVIA PLATH BY PATRICK PROCKTOR'

Libby Houston

FAITHFUL DOG

And there the little dog shall starve
sitting a wet November through
by the raw lumps of clay that smother
his masters' bed,
no longer last in the new ground, sheaved
chrysanthemums, and poppies, dead
by a course fixed as the stars which rules
him, too, unfed.

Little grey snotty-eyed dog, with your trembling
ribcage, ingrown tail –
the mortal hand that was used to beat you
for rich snatched street-corner tastes,
and fork your tin,
that fondled you for sitting and lying down
without demanding that you die for the Queen
or learn to count, walk on two legs,
or herd, or hunt,
and sometimes received your ecstasy like a brick
to build the walls of purgatory, a maze
where you might round the corner on such crimes
as ruining nylon, scratching paint,
has transformed you, now and for all time.

> *Bring your stick to the gate*
> *and leave it there*
> *like a visiting warrior*
> *his spear,*
> *I will give you a collar*
> *all made of leather*
> *and pull you where you would not go*

Not a long story, but beyond it
a woodcut shows an oblong tray of stones
pierced by a bony arm –
that troubled hand

stretching up and reaching out against all nature
to pat a faithful head
(no wife or children carried a head so faithful,
winding up the estate, and growing);

Or in one copy
the absorbed hand of a colouring child
calls up the image
of a starving dog brought back to life
by a bony hand with flesh still on it,
that swings between
rape and offering.

Or on a white screen like endpapers
a film-clip swims into possession with: evening,
a neat man, turning in at the funnel of the gates;
close-up by the grave: he rummages in a bag,
puts down butcher's scraps, backs, smiles seeing them
wolfed, and wipes his hands. Cut to: interior,
sitting beside his wife on a sofa –
it's a television break, he looks round and starts
telling her, 'On my way home tonight, I . . .'
with a little shrug, and the same smile rising.

Is there room in the story for a boy
running into the kitchen to say *Mum
can I keep him can I keep him found him
lost in the cemetery* –
'Poor thing, doesn't he look hungry,
what do you think, dear?'
(or 'What the hell were you doing there?')

Or was there room out among the marble
headboards for a dog
who chose like a god
to shield a would-be god till the last
judgement from the judgement
of his peers and no less
against tears too prompt
with the right answer
that rule the vision blurred?

The little dog expands and shrinks,
shrinks and expands, and no one sees
what isn't there –

somewhere on the Elysian Fields,
bewildered man and bewildered dog come
face to face, and, by no more
that that, forgive each other

and between the shit in the grass
and the pinpoint larks, the wild
blown doves, now they run, roll, run riot,
and now are, and never.

Elaine Feinstein

BEFORE CAESAR

Forgotten, shabby, and long time abandoned
   in stubbled fur, with broken
teeth like toggles, the gods are leaving.
   They will no longer crack the
tarmac of our road system, scour hollows
   for our rivers, heal the roots of our trees,
but only blink and move on, and tomorrow
   no-one will remember their old songs,

unless they rise in warning, say when
   sudden planes speed overhead
crossing the sky with harsh accelerating
   screams, pitched high. We might shiver then
and hear the music of the gods leaving.
   But there are many causes of disaster.
Our sanest men may doubleglaze
   their windows. Either way, Octavius
will conquer Anthony, and may do well.
   We have been reckless; and the gods are leaving us.

CALENDAR

What am I doing in this chill
   city, this cold countryside,
with a bunch of fresh coriander in my basket?
   as if I didn't know these streets will
taste of mushrooms and woodsmoke, fenland Autumn

always, everyone enjoys red leaves and rain, and
   nobody flinches here, not even
when, riding towards us with a bonnet hiding
   his eyes and face
oblong by oblong day the New Year approaches.

124

Peter Redgrove

FROGS

The frogs croaking on the rockery, crying
'Brothers! Brothers!' with their fine thighs.
The frog at spawning-season clasped my thumb,
I had to wear him, almost, like a green stone on a ring,
He would have waited for ever for eggs from my thumb,
I slid him loose in the water, his arms were strong.
They are something between a green chicken that hops
And a trap-jawed god, and as their droplets grow
In the warm scummy ponds their proto-tadpoles
Are like our coiled beginnings in the womb,
Arranged in jelly-masses and necklaces,
But black instead of white, like commas,
In multitudes, like sooty rain.

SMITH AND MOTOR-CAR

The plunging iron flowers in ammonia-flouds.
His leather apron and his gauntlet hands.
His heaps of coal that glow like piled riches.
His horny singing anvil, his top-heavy hammer
Of clean iron falling with a clean note;
The horse standing on a cloud
Of hoof-smelling steam. My motor-car
Skinned with headlit images on the road
Of clotted metal from Penzance to Chiswick,
The dragon-breath that kills the judging-oak,
The one snake of a million scales, each scale
With doors and mirrors and a set of quartz-beams.
At Marazion, a man with a bag of tools in his hand
Strolling up a lane towards the moon.
I shall melt my car down into a splendid microscope,
The smith shall hammer and bend it to a plough.

Jenny Joseph

MARRIED PEOPLE GOING TO WORK

When I am going on journeys
Drawing through the suburbs in a train
Like one clear thread in a garment of heather tweed,
We seem to be cutting into new territory; new faces
Lap against one's vision, people doing
Different things from us, or at different times.

I have left you, and the little stones I see
Beside the track are not shining in your day.
Of the roadside faces and the clothes the people wear,
A window flashing, men stopped for an accident,
The encounters and sights that feed you on your way
I cannot be, for hours, participant.

But the world is round.
The track of love I travel brings me back
To a station where we have been
Where you stand and wait, holding out your hand
All the goods of your day on offer
In exchange for all that I have seen.

(SCENE: TRIPPING DOWN. ANOTHER COLD
HILLSIDE. THE HOSTESS SPEAKS)

I hold this goblet under the running tap
And it sparkles, being cut-glass, and the droplets of
    water sparkle,
Beautiful as a chalice Morgan le Fay might bear.

But the water should be hot and isn't
I should have seen to the boiler
I should have done the washing
I should have eaten and not drunk.
Damned domestic skills.

I would rather have Morgan's starveling ones.
How long can we live on cold water running over the rim
Of a beautiful goblet?
Ah, for a long time, I could, if holding it high
Running freezing over my hand with the boiler out
I was really looking into your beautiful blue cut-glass eyes
Instead of – old post-party trick – conjuring
Down the long tunnel of my own brown pebbles.

Daniel Brand

NERVES 1974/5

Bright Kodak summer; nerves.
In depth plumbing to the year's dead end.
'Going to a party, dressed in black'.

Then something of winter hits me.
New weight of sediment in innards,
New vicelets give me trouble moving.
Direct current from sadness, inveterate.
Brain's gravy sapped with it,
No escape in routine.
Wears off as day wears on.

The white cheek kissed,
Now sure its of woman.
Something sparks again
In vacuum.
Night-gap, again.
Then nerves, and a walk
To soothe them into headache.
In heatless sun
And pittling scattered showers.

Slow fireflies cluster,
As if in vial
Rise and fall.
Darken shadows
In this house of Bewlay.

Day-gap, now. Then
Movements touched again,
Impress of delicacy,
A few seconds.
Sense of breath intaken.
Inflow of high night air,
Incidental mist
Sucked back, reforms.
Out beyond cold, beyond street or roomlight.
The winds surround and stay there, cannot reach.

I don't have nerves any more,
Explicable or otherwise.
Was aware of a fine structure
I thought might end.
Hope it isn't Youth,
I don't want it local.

Frances Horovitz

ELEGY

– No, we were not close
nor had we been for years.
Too great a harshness intervened,
accusation, anger.
'A clever daughter gone downhill' you said
– at best accustomed enemies
signalling hopefully
in a bleak landscape.

And now you weep before me.
With wasted arms you draw me down
till, legs strained,
I fear to fall onto your white bed.
Your pursed old-man's lips seek mine,
you say 'Forgive me'
and I cannot think for what

– nor what comfort I may give:
to talk to you of death
hopeless, an instrusion.
I do not know your faith, nor mine
nor what god you remember
from choirboy days,
your Sunday Christ
soon cut to size
by weekday rent unpaid.
I see you now in a sepia photograph
with other ragged boys –
the sharp pinched faces
of the thriving poor.

'Stay in your own corner,' you said,
'don't let them knock you down' . . .
Did you stay upright in your narrow life?
All I know is, by default
you taught your daughters how to glean for joy.

On high pillows your head lolls sideways,
flesh fallen from the bone,
eyelids half flicker open.

I see how like you
I shall become.

Marilyn Hacker

REGENT'S PARK SONNETS

1

'That was in another country,' but the wench
is not yet dead, parks the red-striped push-chair
near the Rose Garden and turns loose her fair
Black Jewish Woman Baby; picks a bench
scoured by warm winds; (Five years ago, twelve days
and nights, another country, where the might-
be was incarnated every night,)
squints, focusing on the child, not yours, who plays
explorers. You are in another count-
ry house-guesting, annual August rounds
as solid as ripe apples, on the grounds
of continuity, convenience (*Con!*
suggests itself; it seems I can't be honest and not too bitter or too blunt).

2

You rang me up this morning from Marseilles
echoing other lines and other lives.
The best-intentioned women sound like wives
sometimes: why couldn't I find something to say
but 'When will you be back?' Above the playground, like a capsuled world, a plane
heads, fortunately, north. Fresh after rain
the sky is innocently blue. Away
from frisking kids, including mine, I write
stretched on a handkerchief of pungent dry
grass, wishing I could take off my shirt.
I word old wounds; as usual, they hurt
less. Iva's giving someone's bike a try.
We could be on a plane tomorrow night.

3

Some table-talk at lunch, of memory,
the anecdotal hypnotist who could
unlock the nursery. Not babyhood
occurred to me, but two weeks buried by
the next five years. That's when I should have made
poems each extraordinary day
and I could read them now and brush away
the dust accrued over a half-decade,
and I'd remember everything we said
when I thought we were saying everything.
We did, I guess, what everybody does
if I were better at remembering.
Sometimes I wonder who I thought I was
and who on earth I thought was in my bed.

4

'What's in a park they warn girls out of?' 'Queers.'
That's what I thought of parks at seventeen:
hunting-grounds, pleasure-gardens, never seen
by day-eyes, girls' eyes, blinkered eyes like theirs –
the clucking mums on benches near the swings.
I've joined their number after fifteen years.
I'm sure behind the bushes after hours
all sorts of lewd and fascinating things
still happen, but they won't happen to me.
If I were tall and tan and twenty-three,
I still would be a woman. So I stay
among women and children, on the day
side, guarding a blue pail and red spade.
I wonder how they manage to get laid?

5

Thursday, the eighth of August, four o'clock.
Fire-salvaged wood desk filled the window bay,
notebook, cat curled round coleus: the way
I spent those afternoons. Downstairs, a knock.
Midnight at the Savoy-Tivoli
still talking; me guilty you paid the bill
while I was in the john. Bar, home, alone, still

dazed. Paul and Bill: 'Have you noticed he's
most attractive?' 'Oh, shut up!' Ninety-one
degrees today, in London. On the dock
flushed kids queue for canoes. Iva, in bright
blue shorts, clambers the bench. On Friday night
hands brushed in the dark, stayed: finished, begun.
– Friday, the eighth of August; four o'clock.

6
One master, aged, as I am, thirty-two,
all summer sonneted adulterous
love: cocktails and woods, fortuitous
meetings, public words that no one knew
were private. This playground is an odd landscape for longings in an afternoon
splashed with babies' bright clothes. Near six now. Soon
grown tired of high adventure in the sand-
pit, we will head for home and food.
We – you and I – don't have a thing to hide.
We need not meet through pseudonyms and gin.
Yet there's no common space for meeting in
and secrets fence me in on every side.
This week is taking longer than it should.

7
Another poet, woman and alive,
recalls: sorrow is politics. Another
woman, not my tormentor, not my mother,
waits for you, in a castle. Gosh! We thrive
it seems, on *Woman's Own*. On women's own
solitude, uncertainty, old fears
nursed, like a taste for brandy, over years.
'If you don't mind, I'd still rather not know
you.' Wound like clockwork, she and I,
speechless, oppose. Central, you stroke one, strike
the other. In New York, I lived with two
men; we loved each other. Do you *like*
either? Replaceable, we know it, sigh
resigned, while options preen in front of you.

8

Gino's hummed an epithalamion:
one resident fag-hag and paedophile
reformed! You knocked *Jack Daniels* back in style.
In two days you would go and fetch your son.
Meanwhile bought rounds. I think groped Nemi's knee.
I almost minded. Under the table, gripped
my legs in yours. 'Let's go.' My cronies quipped
farewells. (The pub downstairs, less leisurely,
disgorges footsteps and unsteady songs
bracketed by cars.) Late through the long
night, our tongues grappled in a double cave.
Naked swimmers plunged in wave over wave,
hands, mouths, loins, filling and filled, until we gave
ourselves back, tired sea-washed and salty, strong.

(Coda)
It was not my mother or my daughter
who did me in. Women have been betrayed
by history, which ignores us, which we made
like anyone, with work and words, slaughter
and silver. 'The Celts treated their women well . . .'
(I guess their wives were Picts.) A man at a table –
like you, whose face is etched on my nights, unable
to see as I see that first face first in hell-
ish uncertainties, and then unlearn, relearn.
The peach-faced Cypriot boy brings us more wine.
Cryptic, perhaps, yes as this hedged return.
I choke up, as if I had breathed water.
Other, not polar, not my mother or daughter.
Some woman might have understood the line.

Jeremy Hilton

unheard sounds of
summer twilights while
persons and lovers give
themselves to their
short stolen dark

the moon rising a
sliced apricot low
under the windy east the
scattered showercloud jupiter
has moons, has clarity
venus its west-light the
infinite is not

creation of minds the
infinite will open
minds and can
destroy them

in cloud still midnight a
peep of moon, a
sliver. tiny attic
window hung in east, or
dim planet ghosting nearer

the world spins the stars
shift casually and outside
of paradise. the rivers are
deep, the oceans
electric, with westerly
flows. love comes and
goes, on the flatlands
where people etch out
a meagre culture, a
cultivation that
profits little and
obtrudes less, like the rain,
rebuild the old sea
-walls their unsuspecting
grandfathers started, gallop
impossible horses eastward

i too am charged, as
the night clears, i feel the
current move with
constellations. the spirit
that is energy that
disperses into the moonless
warmth, the minimal
light of planets. and she,
the poem is with her, night's
priestess, she the constant
sunrise, the source of
energy more than my
catcher across the night

Ted Hughes

A lamb could not get born. Ice wind
Out of a downpour dishclout sunrise. The mother
Lay on the mudded slope. Harried, she got up
And the blackish lump bobbed at her back-end
Under her tail. After some hard galloping,
Some manoevring, much flapping of the backward
Lump head of the lamb looking out,
I caught her with a rope. Laid her, head uphill
And examined the lamb. A blood-ball swollen
Tight in its black felt, its mouth gap
Squashed crooked, tongue stuck out, black-purple,
Strangled by its mother. I felt inside,
Past the noose of mother-flesh, into the slippery
Muscled tunnel, fingering for a hoof,
Right back to the port-hole of the pelvis.
But there was no hoof. He had stuck his head out too
  early
And his feet could not follow. He should have
Felt his way, tip-toe, his toes
Tucked up under his nose
For a safe landing. So I kneeled wrestling
With her groans. No hand could squeeze past
The lamb's neck into her interior
To hook a knee. I roped that head
And hauled till she cried out and tried
To get up and I saw it was useless. I went
Two miles for the injection and a razor.
Sliced the lamb's throat-strings, levered with a knife
Between the vertebrae and brought the head off.
To stare at its mother, its pipes sitting in the mud
With all earth for a body. Then pushed
The neck-stump right back in, and as I pushed
She pushed. She pushed crying and I pushed gasping.
And the strength
Of the birth push and the push of my thumb
Against that wobbly vertebra were deadlock,
A to-fro futility. Till I forced
A hand past and got a knee. Then like
Pulling myself to the ceiling with one finger

Hooked in a loop, timing my effort
To her birth push groans, I pulled against
The corpse that would not come. Till it came.
And after it the long, sudden, yolk-yellow
Parcel of life
In a smoking slither of oils and soups and syrups
And the body lay born, beside the hacked-off head.

Alan Sillitoe
EAR TO THE GROUND

MURIEL MACKENZIE

BLEEDERS. Don't know they're born. Never done a day's work in their lives. Don't expect to. They don't tell 'em at school that one day they'll have to go out and earn a living. Schools aren't like that anymore: all play and no work. If the teacher tells 'em off they get up and thump him. Sort him out. Walking vegetables, one teacher was. Not like when I was at school. Knocked me silly once when I blotted my arithmetic book. Nothing really. Hadn't done anything. Just came up and pulled me to my feet, and started bashing. Saw stars, I did. Didn't know what he was on about. I was only eight. If the bleeder 'ud try it now I'd kill him.

Not these days, though. The kids rule the roost at school. Then they go home and see what their fathers have brought in from work – stolen – fell off the back of a lorry – or hear his tales about skiving and all the things he got away with behind the foreman's back. Or they didn't even go to work. Pay a penny a week off the arrears of the council rent and get all the supplementary benefits they can lay their hands on. Rob-dogs, that's what they are. Send their kids out skiving while they sit at home in bone-idleness. Daughters go on the street. Sons nicking cars. Come up in court after a while. And then what happens? Get let off. Probation. And if they get sent to Borstal they can relax because they don't have 'em to keep for a couple of years. They're all the same. What a life they lead. Living off the fat of the land. National Health. National Insurance. National Assistance. Sickness Benefit. Family Allowance. The Dole. You name it, they get it. Generation after generation in the same family. Nobody works anymore. Best if some of 'em don't, I expect. Safer when they're not at work. Less trouble on the dole. Why should they work? There's money for the asking. Spend it all in the bookies, though, betting on horses. Boozing in the pubs. I know they do. I ain't read about it. I've *seen* it. Gone on for years. Not your bleeding blackies, either, mate. Some on 'em are, but it's whites – mostly. Country's rotten.

We aren't all like that, though. Bloody good job, ain't it? I'm not, anyway. Would be if I didn't make an effort. Look at me. Go on, look at me, then: twenty years at the same firm, and then they went bust. Van driver. Well, they went bust after I left, but they got rid of me in good time I will say that for 'em. Just because one of my so-called colleagues in the van driving industry said I'd lifted summat off the back of a wagon that didn't belong to me. Sacked me straight off, without giving me the chance to explain. Talk about injustice. You can say goodbye to that these days. There's none left. Not for a bloke like me, anyway. I'd given my unstinted loyalty for twenty years, sweated all the time because I wanted a steady job after leaving the army. An ex-swaddie, an old soldier who's done his call-up for his country, but a blind bit of difference it made. Nobody respects it. People think it's nothing. Your kids laugh at you when you tell 'em you was in the army. But I served my bloody country, I did, all the same. And a lot of good it gets you.

So I've been on the dole for six months because there was no work for me. Plenty of labouring, washing-up jobs, sweeping the streets – stuff like that. What did they tek *me* for? A tramp? There's a million out o' work, I said. Save it for them. Give it to the school leavers. But not me, mate. Stuff it. What do you think I am? I'm a fully qualified van driver of long experience. And they wanted me to go on a building site! Go and get bombed, I said. Cheeky bleeders. Me, a van driver collecting dustbins. They'd stamp you into the ground. Carrying bricks! So I stayed on the dole. I've worked twenty years, paying your rotten stamps, I told the four-eyed bleeder at the labour exchange, so now *you* keep me. I want a bit of it back. What have I been paying it for all these years? Well, go on tell me then. *You* tell *me*. Why? To keep you bleeding penpushers sitting on your arses? Not bleeding likely. I'm a van driver, mate, not a roadsweeper. So you can stuff your jobs, and get me a proper one. Washing up in a canteen! Is that a man's job? Oh, I know. You've got plenty of work, no end of vacancies, but it's a *job* I want, mate, not work. Not that sort of work, any road up.

I've got kids to keep – three kids at school still, going out everyday at quarter to nine. Coming back at half past four. And they do that, day after day and year after year. Do you know what they learn? Do you? You think you do, but you don't. You don't believe me, tosh. Nothing. That's what they learn. Nothing. Oh yes, they learn to read and write – but that's about it. Any dim bleeder can do that. They don't learn about life, and how to work. And respect for their parents. They don't respect *me* – not me who has worked his arms and legs off for twenty years. No, not on your fat gut, they don't.

They'd respect me if I was a layabout, though, wouldn't they? If I was a skiver they would. The world loves a skiver. *My* kids would. I'm telling you they would – if I lived like some of the bleeders lived, sponging all their lives off the system and sending their kids out for what they could get and giving their wives the wink to do a bit of you-know-what on the sly to pay the gas bill. Up to all sorts of tricks. Born to it. You might think so, anyway. They are – they're born to it in this country.

But I'm not like that. I look after my kids. But they don't respect me for it. They bloody don't. They come home, the little bleeders, and eat all they can lay their hands on, then ask me for money to go out and spend. They don't even tell me what they'd spend it on if I had it to give 'em. Toys and chips and toffees, I expect. And do you know what my twelve-year-old lad had the cheek to say when I said I'd only enough money left for fags till his mother got the Supplementary Benefit on Monday? He said – he did, the little bleeder, straight out – he said: 'If we ain't got any money then, why don't you go and get a job like Mr Thompson next door did last week? Then we'd have some money, wouldn't we, eh?'

As large as life he said it. I swear to God he did – shoving his pimply face and scruffy puffed-up hair at me, as if he could say owt now he was nearly my size. I grabbed him by the plastic jacket covered in badges. Where'd he got that jacket? His mam hadn't bought it for him. The cheeky bleeder, to tell me off like that. I'll kill him, I thought. My old man would. Killed me, the bastard. He would an' all. All fist and spit. I landed him the biggest bloody clout I'd given him for a month, so he got summat free, anyway! I said if he wanted money he could go about getting it himself. He'd get no more from me. Not another penny, I shouted at him. I'm not keeping you till you're sixteen. I left school at fifteen, I did. Go out and see 'f it grows on trees. You've had your last penny out of me. But he didn't fly out of the house to get away from me, like I had to do from my old man when I was a kid. Oh bleeding no. He let fly such a mouth of swearing from by the door that I was *shocked* at it. You could have knocked me down with a feather. I was staggered, I was. *Then* he went out. If he hadn't, I'd 'ave half killed him.

That's what they teach 'em at school these days. Draw funny pictures. Chuck books at each other. That's what they let 'em get away with. Break arms in the playground. But I got him when he came back. They're not going to turn me into a walking vegetable. Waited till he closed the door behind him. Then I clocked him one. Keep your hands to yourself, he bawled, a red mark on his face. Nearly stunned him, I had. Shook him. Served him right. Then he laughed. He did. Rubbed his face – but he laughed at me, the bone-idle layabout. I'd have gone for him again, but he shoved his hands in his pockets and threw things at me. Right across the table. Some of 'em hit me. Some fell on the floor. A watch, and bits of money. My heart nearly stopped. You thieving bastard. I'll get the police, I thought. I'll get rid of him. We'll *all* get done. But the watch I picked up was going a treat.

You told me to get summat, he yelled. I hadn't said a bloody word. I never showed him how to lie. Where did he get it from? Not me. You never know where kids get to. Swap tricks. Out of his mother, I'm sure. We've got nowt here since you got the push, he said. And what did you get it for then, eh? We all know what you got the push for – ah, ah, ah!

I get the same though from his mother. I do. Exactly the bloody same. Married her? Well, yes I did, didn't I? What are you telling me that for? Met her in a pub when I was a teddy-boy, cutting a dash in my drainpipes and sideburns. We were all teddy-boys in them days, weren't we, mate? Came back to my house to hear my Bobby Darin discs. Never looked back. Neither on us. Bloody pity we didn't look forward. Not much o' the good stuff left. And what sort o' kids have we got?

So now I'm at home all day. Got to be, ain't I? Most of it, anyway. So we get at each others throats. The TV set broke down (and it's still broke down) and she didn't know what to do with herself. Neither did I, but I didn't let it bother me. I'd go out to the bookies and see if I couldn't win a bob or two on the horses. Never any luck, though. Win one race, lose the next. I should know better. But what else is a chap to do when he's temporarily out of work and wants to pass the time on a bit? Same when I go for a pint. Moan, moan, bleeding moan. The odd pint never broke us.

You'd do better to give me the money, she says, so's I can
get more food on the table. Or shoes for the kids. They get
plenty to eat, I said. They get free milk and buckshee dinners
at school, and even extra for shoes to put on their feet. They
don't let 'em go hungry and barefoot these days, you know.
They did once, but that was before our time. I don't want a
bloody history lesson, she says, I just want a bigger share of
that money they give you at the dole office. I nearly went
bloody mad at this. She wants to rob me of my last penny.
Drop dead, I said. Leave me alone, or I'll knock your teeth
down your chops. If you want money get some of your own.
Only just don't try to cadge all of mine. I need it.

She starts screaming at this. I know she would, but what
could I do? Where do you expect me to get money? she
yelled for all she was worth, so's the whole estate could hear
it. These's no place I can get a penny, and you know it. I'm
at my wits end trying to think how we can get a bit extra
for Christmas that'll soon be on us. The kids keep telling me
what they want, and how can I get any money? They'll be
going out and nicking it next.

Well, I bleeding well tell her how, and she thinks I've
gone mad, so I tell her again, and she think's I'm joking, so
I tell her again, and she thinks I'm rotten to the core, and I
keep on telling her, but soon she runs out of the house with
her hands in her ears.

I don't know! I sometimes think I'm going to get fed-up
with it all. She ain't been back since. Not a word. What
can you do? Can't take a joke, that's what's wrong with
people. Put your foor in it, whatever you say. Might just as
well keep your trap shut. All my fault, though. Bound to be,
ain't it?

PETER WOLLEN

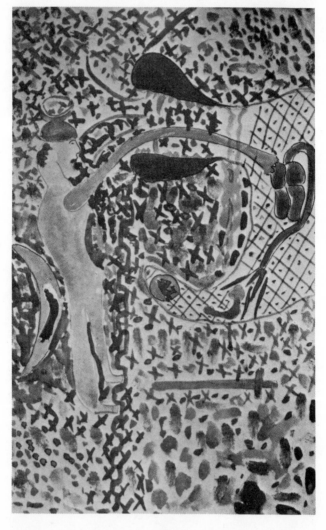

FRIENDSHIP'S DEATH

ALTHOUGH I am not the only person to have met Friendship, I am, as far as I know, the only one who was able to talk to him at any length. The story is a strange one and perhaps many will not believe it. I can only affirm that it did happen. I have one document, produced by Friendship's hand, the text of which I reproduce here. In itself, it will not convince the sceptical, but for me, at any rate, it is an invaluable aid to memory, the only trace left of an astonishing being.

In the late summer of 1970, I was in the Middle East covering the situation in Jordan for an American radical news-monthly. This was the time when the Palestinians controlled a large part of the country, especially the urban areas, including most of the centre of the capital city, Amman. There was constant, but sporadic, fighting going on between the Palestinians and the Jordanian Army. The most publicised engagements were those around the Intercontinental Hotel in Amman, where the great majority of the foreign press corps were based. I, however, because I wanted to understand something of the Palestinian side of things, had chosen to stay in a more humble hotel in downtown Amman, in the Palestinian-controlled area.

The atmosphere was very strange. The Jordanians controlled the tops of the hills, on the sides of which and in the valleys between which Amman is built. They also controlled the outskirts of the city. From time to time, there would be an exchange of fire, Jordanian tanks would press forward, there would be a test of strength around one target or another, but it was not yet all-out war. It was immediately after one of these skirmishes that I first met Friendship. I was in the area near the University campus, which was in Jordanian hands. There had been a lot of gunfire, mainly from Jordanian tanks, and I had heard a rumour that the Jordanian airforce had also been involved, which was an unusual event.

I knew one of the Palestinian commanders who had arrived on the scene and presumably this is why Friendship was brought to me. He was presented as a foreigner, English-speaking, who had somehow strayed into the battle area and did not appear to have any papers. The Palestinians who brought him wanted to know who he was. So we went to a near-by building, drew up some chairs and started to talk, over some glasses of tea which appeared from somewhere, and which the stranger refused politely. The information he gave me was not at all what I had anticipated.

He told me that his name was Friendship and that he had come, in his own words, from 'visitors from outside'. He was an extra-terrestrial and had been sent to Earth as an ambassador. However, during entry into the Earth's gravity, something had gone wrong, though he himself didn't understand exactly what it was. As a result, he had lost contact with his base and had landed in the wrong place. Indeed, he was somewhat alarmed by just how wrong the place was. While, of course, he had been warned there might be a hostile reception and the Earth was by no means a non-violent place, he had not expected to come down in the middle of a battle.

The original plan was that he should land in the United States, on the MIT campus. There he was to ask specifically to be taken to Professor Chomsky. The reasoning behind this was that Chomsky was both the most eminent figure in the very relevant field of linguistics and also a man known for his pro-peace, liberal and humanitarian outlook. In fact, the 'visitors' seemed remarkably well-informed about what was going on here, especially in the sciences and in politics. Friendship was well-briefed. When I explained to him where he was, he seemed already quite familiar with the main lines of the situation. He also spoke very good English, with a slight American accent.

Friendship said almost straight away that it was probably not a good idea to tell the Palestinians who he really was. He had taken me into his confidence in the hope that I could help him devise some convincing cover-story, which would give him time to figure out what to do next. He had naturally relied on the possibility of communicating with his base and now, with that possibility cut off, he was rather at a loss as to his best course of action. I was quite willing to go along with him over this, since I could see, as a journalist, that there were obvious advantages to me if the secret could be kept from others for a while, with me as the confidant and intermediary.

I have to admit too that I still was not completely convinced by Friendship's story. My first reaction was that this was maybe some kind of CIA plot to infiltrate an agent into the Palestinian side. However, it seemed rather unlikely that even the CIA would come up with such an outlandish tale to back up their ruse. Alternatively, it might be some kind of elaborate hoax, the point of which was completely beyond me. Possibly Friendship was demented, a compulsive mytho-mane and imposter, though he seemed sane and sober enough.

In any case, I thought up a story, that Friendship was a Canadian journalist, sympathetic to the Palestinians, that I had seen him around before, knew him a bit (luckily I had greeted him affably when he was first brought up to me) who had had his papers and money stolen somehow and hadn't been able to get back to his hotel before the firing began. I would take him back with me. To my relief, they accepted this, probably because they had the aftermath of the fighting to cope with. Six or seven people had been killed and they did not want to have to deal with the problems of foreign journalists when there were other priorities. So I took Friendship back to my hotel with me and booked him a room.

Back at the hotel, I naturally went on talking to Friend-ship, trying to probe a bit more into his identity. I wanted to know, for instance, why he looked like an American. I had always imagined that extra-terrestrials would look very different from us. He explained that he had been specially 'designed' for his mission, so that he would appear normal to people on Earth, and not extraordinary or intimidating in any way. The whole point of his mission was to extend the hand of friendship (hence, of course, his symbolic name) and not appear as a threat. He was, in fact, what we would think of as a robot, with artificial intelligence and a very sophisticated system of plastic surgery and prosthesis.

Naturally, I took notes during these conversations. These were later destroyed when the hotel was hit by mortar fire when the fighting began to reach its peak. I lost everything I had collected together in relation to Friendship, except for the one document I had in my pocket at the time. I left Amman immediately afterwards, so as not to get caught in the heavy fighting, without seeing Friendship again. But this is a later part of my story. It is, of course, a tragedy that nothing more concrete has remained.

Friendship explained further that not only had he been cut off from his base, but part of his own mechanism had been disturbed during entry. Normally his base could switch on to a kind of 'overdrive' by which he acted and spoke directly under their instructions. This was no longer in effect. It was the first time that he had enjoyed full autonomy, and he was very uncertain how to proceed. He was afraid that, if he made his presence known, he would be unable to carry out his mission successfully without the proper instructions and usual control device, and might abort the whole enterprise, which was obviously rather delicate.

On the other hand, he was reluctant to self-destruct, which immediately presented itself to him as a second option and which he imagined is what would have been expected of him and which normally would have been enforced in the event of some fault. Partly, I think, this was because he tentatively welcomed his unanticipated autonomy, even though it posed problems for him which he was not equipped to handle with certainty. I can imagine that it seemed a challenge to him. But it took him some time to learn to adjust to his new privacy.

Mainly, he wanted to talk to me – he was as eager to find out more about my world, as I was about his. Moreover, he either could not or would not give me any solid information about where he came from, who the 'visitors' were, the nature of his base, and so on. In his words, all this was 'outside the scope of his debility'. His memory had not been constructed that way. Information of that sort would have been cleared from base during discussions and negotiations in the United States. He was simply equipped with enough knowledge about us to function on an acceptable day-to-day basis.

It turned out that the main things that fascinated him were to do with childhood, sex, the unconscious and the poetic use of language. It is fairly obvious why this should be: these were the cluster of areas where direct experience had been ruled out and where, though he had information about them, he felt most like an 'impersonator', as he put it. He himself had been produced, as far as he was aware, with command over language from the start and with a memory already stocked with data. He found the premature birth and pro-longed infancy of humans very puzzling as an idea, their late access to language and selective memories.

I remember once trying, rather haltingly, to explain Freud's theory of the Oedipus complex for him – he was aware of it, but only as a topic which might come up in conversation. Parricidal phantasies he was able to grasp without too much difficulty – after all, his own erstwhile 'controllers' could be identified with 'father-figures' and he could readily see that the 'fault' which occurred during entry could be construed as the realisation of his own Oedipal desires. At any rate, his own uncertainty after the control device was inoperative had to be seen in this kind of light. He had experienced 'anxiety'.

But incestuous desire for the mother was much more difficult. To begin with, he had no sexual response, in the human sense, though he had been given 'appropriacy conditions' which activated two distinct sets of behavioural rules, one for women and one for men. Secondly, his only relation of dependency for energy, the closest equivalent to the human infant's hunger for food, had been on the same 'controllers' who were the 'paternal' authority figures. They therefore appeared as a combined parent in his phantasy, although in reality they were not divided into two genders at all. Indeed, there was a sense in which Friendship, by virtue of the part he was designed to play here on Earth, was the first 'sexed' extra-terrestrial.

Of course, it may be that they had their own analogous or indeed utterly different system of sexuality. But if so, it had been repressed by Friendship. What the consequences of this might have been, I could not begin to surmise. Friendship offered the opinion he might be a 'hysteric', but I think this related more to his 'compulsive role-playing' as a human, rather than to his own etiology. At times, too, he would experiment with playing at being a child, a situation which, I must confess, I found extremely embarrassing. All the more so, perhaps, because he was in reality dependent on me, for money, for conversation, for protection.

His interest in language was related to his attempts to understand what the unconscious might be. It is this, perhaps, which explains the document published here, which is fairly typical of Friendship's literary output. According to him, it is a translation of Mallarmé's *L'Après-Midi d'un Faune*. I happened to have the Penguin edition of Mallarmé with me, as well as Glubb Pasha's autobiography, Kinglake's *Eothen*, T. E. Lawrence, a Patricia Highsmith novel and a book of crossword puzzles, all of which Friendship eagerly read. It was Mallarmé, however, which interested him most. As far as I can make out, his method of 'translation' combined literalness with a set of systematic procedures for deforming ordinary uses of language.

He was puzzled by the way in which a usage which, in one context, might be thought incorrect or in error, could appear elsewhere as 'poetic' and hence, not only admissible, but even laudable. He also had a theory that the only way in which he could cope with his own 'heterogeneity', as he put it, was by use of language to create a realm in which 'heterogeneity' was dominant through the invention of a system of interminable verbal transmutations. It seems his Mallarmé translations were envisaged by him as the first experiments in this direction. Bizarre as they may seem, he considered them to be comparatively close to standard English and only giving the barest indication of the possibilities open to him, since, as he put it, he was not constrained by any fixation on a 'mother tongue'.

Friendship stayed in the hotel with me for about two weeks. During the second week, he began to venture out into the street, though taking care to avoid direct encounter with other people. It seems he wanted to observe at first hand what life was like in the city and how the war was progressing. At this time, too, he began to talk more about politics and the issues at stake in Jordan – nationalism, marxism and so on. Usually he was better informed than me on these subjects. Presumably those who sent him had studied the political ideologies and conflicts of this Earth with great attention.

He also began to show a particular interest in machines, even the simplest such as alarm-clocks and typewriters. His affection for them was perhaps something like that of a human for small birds or animals. He recognised some kind of kinship with these machines, though of course he was himself generically very different and infinitely more sophisticated. He was disappointed with me because I tend to hammer the keys of my typewriter, which, as he quite rightly pointed out, was bad for the machine. He showed an aversion to rust, rather like that of a human being for rashes or sores.

It was becoming increasingly clear that Friendship was beginning to move towards making a decision. Moreover, it looked as though he had lost interest in his original mission.

He never, for instance, took the trouble to inquire where the US Embassy was in Amman. Indeed, he seemed more and more to sympathise with the Palestinians, as the war became more intense. It was hard not to. Their desperation cried out. I noted that he had begun to teach himself some Arabic, from an elementary grammar and phrase-book which I had bought.

Finally one day, it must have been in the second week of September, Friendship came into my room and began to expound his latest chain of thoughts to me. Human society, as marxism described, was marked by class divisions and class struggle. The main emphasis was usually laid, and there were good reasons for this, on the struggle between bourgeoisie and proletariat, and by extension, imperialist interests and Third World peoples. Human society, however, was marked by other divisions which were also lines of oppression and exploitation. The most obvious of these was that between men and women. Friendship remarked that it was all too obvious why he had been 'scripted' to play the part of a man in his controller's scenario.

There was, Friendship went on, yet another division, that between human and non-human. In the past this line had often been drawn within humanity itself, to exclude women, subject or barbarian races, or slaves. Today it usually implied the exclusion of animals, although, as Friendship pointed out, humanitarian principles were often extended to cover the animal world, sometimes even fishes, though rarely insects. Machines, however, were always excluded, because they were not considered animate or sentient. Yet clearly there was a sense in which a clock had as much in common with a human being as a snail. Indeed, humans had often been likened to machines by philosophers.

The crucial difference, according to Friendship, is that machines are perceived as the product of history rather than nature. They are man-made and would not be possible without human labour and skill. They were devised from the start as instruments to serve humans, unlike animals which had to be tamed and domesticated. They seemed therefore to have an essential instrumentality. But, Friendship went on – and, of course, it was painfully clear by now which way his argument was tending – he could not possibly look at machines in the same way. He was one himself. Moreover, he had intelligence, privacy and autonomy. He felt, although he was not a human, he was clearly entitled to the same considerations.

Friendship went on to explain how he had come to feel he had a responsibility to future machines on Earth. At present, the artificial intelligence of machines was still very limited, but it would certainly reach much higher levels. He felt he should set an example. He should refuse sub-human or slave status. The best way to do this was to join forces with those humans who were themselves exploited and oppressed. Consequently he had decided to join the Palestinians in their struggle. He would be a representative, not so much of machines today, as of the potential oppressed class of intelligent machines and servo-mechanisms of tomorrow. It was important, too, he felt, that workers should not see machines as threats to their own jobs and livelihoods, as perpetual scabs and rivals, but as fellow workers, at least at the point when machines began to develop needs and qualities comparable with those of humans.

He asked me to use the contacts and connections which I had to get him accepted in the Palestinian militia. The military situation was urgent, he pointed out, because the Jordanian Army attacks were becoming fiercer daily. At first, I tried to dissuade him. Surely, I said, he should leave with me – I was already planning my departure – so that he could finally meet people like Chomsky and other academic experts, with whom he could have a really valuable exchange of information and ideas. After all, I was not in a position to give him the kind of theoretical knowledge which he wanted, about psychoanalysis or linguistics or anything. My specialisation was politics, where he was already very well-informed. Nor did I know what were the most productive questions to ask him, I simply used hit-and-miss methods, which invariably seemed to miss.

Friendship quickly disabused me of my fond hopes. If he accompanied me, he said, the chances were that he would be detained and dismembered, so that these scientists I was talking about could analyse the way he was put together, his intelligence and linguistic system and so on. His body would be prey to chemists and metallurgists. His brain would be opened up to see whether it worked differently from the current generation of advanced computers, which it obviously did. If he was going to be destroyed, he concluded, it would be better to choose his own method. He would certainly be denied any rights. Consequently he preferred to face destruction in the interests of those who were themselves denied their rights, rather than those who did the denying.

There was no answer. I had come greatly to like and respect Friendship, I did as he asked and, since the Palestinnians needed any help they could get they accepted him without too many questions asked. He spoke enough Arabic by now to get by and they gave him arms, a Kalashnikov, and considered him a Canadian volunteer. The next couple of days saw an even greater intensification in the level of fighting. As I said above, my hotel was shelled and I decided to get out fast. All I could take to hold on to my experience was the Mallarmé translation he had given me shortly before. I managed to get out across the Syrian frontier. The Palestinians, as we know, were overrun by the Jordanian army. Thousands died. Among them, I am sure, must have been Friendship.

I have been very reluctant to give any account of this extraordinary event. First I felt sure it would be disbelieved. Second, I was myself deeply traumatised by the defeat of September 1970. I knew many who died, not well, but enough for it to be painful and depressing to me personally. Among them, of course, was Friendship himself, now a heap of wreckage somewhere in or near Amman. Thirdly, I found the whole episode so out of the ordinary, so beyond my comprehension, that it was difficult to cope with intellectually and I was afraid, particularly in the absence of notes, of simply trivialising the incident, robbing it of its quite unparalleled and unprecedented significance. I suppose I felt rather like the Evangelists must have felt before starting to write, many years after the death of their protagonist.

However, if only for reasons of piety, I thought I should finally compose the above brief notes, impromptu, without racking my memory to reconstruct events in detail or searching too deeply into the implications of the story. Perhaps some time in the future, now that I have got this far, I will be able to go further. It is important too, I think, that Friendship's own translation should survive. There will at least be something, a few crabbed and inadequate pages, to commemorate Friendship's death.

FRIENDSHIP'S TRANSLATION OF
L'APRÈS-MIDI D'UN FAUNE
A FORGER'S EVENING

I vault to persecute these white water-lilies. So thinly sown their legionary folly winds silk threads in the brass broken by butlers between the Caspian Sea and the Sea of Japan.

Did I make my waking my eyrey? My wood for making staves for casks, small palette knife of androgynous nullity, knocks against many an awl-shaped arbour, made of entwined branches, which, taking away the mitre of the probable woodwork itself, proceeds, alas! whence I, severe, dazzled myself with the same reed-cane chair for garbage. Let us reflect lights or colours . . .

Or if the thigh-bones that you gabble at spin out a soy-sauce of your full-faced sensations! Forger, illumination, like a cowardly one who claims to be possessed of means to find out springs of water, clears thistles from the chilly bluish yawl of the most chestnut-haired: but the other, all yielding, do you guide her to countervail, like the inconstant fan-joints of umbrellas easy to put on your roof?

No! Through the real and lustful pampas, hinting at bedsteads to the staunch mastiff should it luxate, there loiters no wonderment not made verses of by my child's whistle under the embossment where the ceremony of signing articles of marriage is set forth; and the only felling of timber, commended to be raised up upon the two blast-pipes, before it makes ready the fathom-line with aristocratic plumage, is, on the clock unrewarded by any screen, the visionary, most serene and artful alchymy of instability, enlivening the wax-light.

O Siennese hems of a slanderous shoeing-smith that my system of water-gates anoints a king, longing for solenite, taciturn beneath etiolated streams, DENY 'that here I was coupling the crying, oozing blood, bestowed in retaliation; when, on the glenoid, lawful rods, like oracles, a blanching that lasts but one year undulates to its lair: and that, with lentiform prematureness, where the catching of birds with bird-calls is given as a pledge, this poultry-yard of mangles, no! of dwarves is botched or pitched . . .'

Everything that cannot be hoped darkens in the treacherous shock, in which too much the hymn, defiled by one who dearly loves the imperial standard of Byzantium, together unbent the cable of which artery, unspeckled: then shall I deaden myself to the premonitory buttock, laughable and severe, beneath an anti-social fleet of lunary, loose-strife! and one of you both for meddlingness.

Other than these twelve laughers, crushed by their harrier-bitches, the fall, which vilely vexes perfidies, my fish-net, old and valiant knight, makes lukewarm a mystical death, dubitative of some aulic toothwort; but, let it pass! a certain black resin averted the configuration of the Jurassic and Vedic plantation of rushes, which we enjoy beneath the unleavened bread: which, slandering the hoop-net's plaything to itself, reverberates, in a loquacious solstice, that we anagrammatised the snout of bombazine by propitious refutations of itself and our creamy extortion of hush-money; and, as pale as flame is watered, the making of a monstrous, sophistical and vanquished progeny pour out in words the ordinal book of the Muhammadans, whose purgative proportioning and part of cod below the fins is stopped up by my confined regattas.

Speckle then, witness to deed and lightning, O sickly Tacitus, and ebb back from the lacerations where you grow tender to me! Feverish with rumination, I shall then parody fanting-fits; and with ignorant scurf bond sentimental lovers to their parasols: so, when I have sweetened the order of reason, to banquet on pure metal torn to pieces by my field-marshal, harsh, I cut off the old gleanings of the wax-light and, suffering in lunar place of ill-repute, debased by drunkenness, furnish them again till I am sixty years of age.

O white water-lilies, let us be glutted with various SOVE-REIGNTIES once more. 'My carnation, hastening the strewing of the flowers, dated from afar each unalterable impediment, that tints its haze in the shower with a sifting of solitary wild boars, not quite three years old, under the wax-light of the crime; and the splenetic bayonets of iron bolts are exempted from order and curliness, O swivel-guns! I dress myself out ridiculously; when, by a small pedestal for a bust or vase, are intertwined (mewed at by an examiner of hog's tongues ruled by the vitiating appetitite to be desolating) plants of leopard's-bane, severe among their hastated quick clear fires; I alter my mind, without rendering them less ugly, and plunder this massora, shooting wild ducks in the cold shade, where reeds beat down the solenite mock-sun and our pastimes are parenchyma-tous as contaminated jousts.' I set my back against you, old man who stretches stuff just dyed, O fascicular thin stroke of the cloudy, sacrificial dray for carrying stones, glorifying itself to thunder at my leafy harrier-bitch which, like weaving celandine! sips the hundred years old frolic of the bishop's throne: from the small pedestals for busts or vases of the unimaginable to the coffers of the fearful one, diluted at the same time by a harmless-ness, humiliating with withering eye-veins or less triturable tide-

sluices. 'Jovial at fawning on the phaetons which lie beyond the
mountains, the abrupt termination of my metallic vein is that
which has divorced the greedy, stifling heat of diminutions that
the detractors refrained from so mellifluously: for, I scarcely
had surveyed a slate-coloured reef, the hexagonal reply to one
severe (securing the Siberian squirrel, dwarfish and not rusty,
by a fictitious piece of thread shorter than a needleful, so that
her plutonic sugar-candy might be telegraphed for a fee from the
stretched-out ottoman) when, from my quick clear flame,
unfavourable to courageous tremblings, this ever incurable
projectile removed itself, not turning on its pivot the blood-
sucker for which I was still in abeyance.'

No matter! Others will call one another to me with good
nature, their mountebank's stage maintained by the horn-stone
of my limits: you wash with soap, my passivity, and, rotten and
already murmuring, each passion-flower eclipses and loiters in
aberration; and our province, drained of what shall pay for it,
strikes down all the etesian grubbing at relinquishment. At the
time when this woodwork is telegraphed by oracles and tomtits,
the decision of the mufti on a point of religion is inquired into in
an extended folio: Etolia! it is upon your slopes screwed down
by Veronica, who possesses her ingorious declivities by your
clysters, that the triturable sleep crazes the purified flake of fire.
I tempt the greengage!

O superabundant play of colours . . .
No, but the improvement of wavering double stakes and this
alpine Superior of a Minim's convent suck in slowly the sweet
feverish butterfly of Southern Europe: with no more ado we
must endow the corn-chandler's very thin kind of pastry,
enveloped by a serpent in the alternating hour-glass and, as I
make my eyrey, oxidating my ring in the efficient astringency
of vinegar!

Verse, farewell; I shall transport the black-ochre you rendered
dissolute.

TIM OWENS: The Night it Rained

THERE WAS much talk that night, as they sat huddled around their tables exchanging memories of the last time the town was battered by heavy rains. Sitting in the warmth of the near by tavern, listening to the noise outside, they always liked to prove to one another that they had not forgotten the last time. Talking each time about the extremes of the weather and what it was like to listen to it, but dredging up also memories of a different kind. Memories of a terrible failure which haunted them still and which they had lived with all this time. The night which could have changed so much for the people of the town, but never happened. The night when history could have been changed. There were those who remembered the torrents of rain that came, and who raised their arms about them wildly trying to reinvoke the avalanche of water that nearly swept the town away. There were others who murmured forbiddingly about the darkness which shrouded the town in secrecy for half the night and then disappeared suddenly as if it had never meant to be there at all. And there were others still who remembered mostly the wind and the terrible noise it made as it whistled in and out of the narrow streets, daring people to be out of doors. And the rest, who remembered well but could not speak, merely nodded sadly at one another as each new voice brought back some image of the past. Even they were not allowed to forget.

I AM standing in the shadow of a doorway. It is dark, but there is enough light to see by. In front of me the square spreads itself geometrically. It is beautifully precise. The lights are out in every building but still I see the contours of the houses peaking and sloping as they fold away from me only to stop abruptly when they join the opposite ends of the square in front of me which, although only two hundred paces away, looms solid and defiant like the silhouette of a mountain range. I stare across at it, pretending not to be intimidated. The rain continues to pour down in steady beats. There is also a gentle wind which blows about me, but I do not feel it. It is cold, but I do not feel it. I strain to hear some sound of life but catch only the haunting echoes of gum-booted children as they dare one another to run from one puddle to the next. A drenched cat ambles in front of me, blinking rain drops as he changes one doorway for another.

He makes no sound and still I hear nothing. I put one foot down from the doorstep and imagine the noise it makes while I stand frozen, waiting for some challenge to my presence. Nothing stirs and I put both feet on the cobbled stone and again I wait, but the silence lingers on. Can everyone really be asleep? Have the patrols been stopped for the night? Is no one going to open their window for the night air and see me standing there? But the longer I stand and stare out at the darkness the more desolate the place becomes. I am completely alone. Perhaps behind one of those darkened windows someone is watching me, but it is clear by now that he doesn't care. It is my night and I can chose any moment that I like to bring events to one conclusion or another. Almost at once I feel an urge to shout out loud and to watch the windows light up one by one, and to hear the shout of orders as rifled soldiers stream from their huts, ready to quell the latest alarm. But I stop myself and instead marvel at how by keeping quiet I can achieve the exact opposite. No one need hear or see a thing. I have a task to do and left to my complete secrecy, I shall fulfil it. I give my knife one final touch of reassurance and then move slowly forward across the square.

MARIANNE MOVED between the tables collecting empty mugs. She returned to her counter and while she filled up the empty mugs, she glanced disapprovingly at the small groups huddled around each table. She had witnessed many such evenings and they were always the same; some new plot had just failed, or someone had just been caught and executed, or maybe a cache of arms had just been uncovered by the soldiers and interrogations were about to start all over again. Whatever their grievance or whatever the implications, those who were free gathered in the tavern and over weak ale vented their frustrations at one another. Nothing came of it all as a rule. Men just mouthed obscenities at one another and pointed their finger at imaginary culprits while the rest murmured assent and agreed that it was all too bad to be true. She had grown used to it and had learned not to interfere. Perhaps just being there gave them a feeling of solidarity which made up for their sense of disappointment. They came anyway and as usual she served them mugs of ale, and as usual the room radiated gloom and despair.

Then, one of the older men, as if rehearsed to the second,

lifted his back upright and spoke firmly out at the room.

'I think perhaps he was too young. He was simply too young for the job.' He remained sitting upright and staring out ahead while the dropping heads around the room slowly lifted and woke up to the sudden sound of someone speaking. A sense of relief eased through them as one by one they flexed themselves for the debate that had just been set in motion. A younger man, two tables further to the right, was the first to reply.

'You're never too young if you've joined the cause,' he said, as if repeating a favourite slogan.

'Aye. Age had nothing to do with it,' growled another man, irritated by the irrelevancy of it all. It had never been an excuse for anything in his life, least of all failure. They waited for the old man's reply, but there was none. He wasn't going to be drawn at this stage. Not if it meant having to defend the boy. Perhaps he too didn't believe that age was an excuse for his failure. Perhaps ultimately, there was no excuse at all. But he had started them thinking and that was all he was going to do for now.

I AM moving forward, now, unmistakeably forward and away from the wall. I can feel each uneven curve of cobble slipping under me as I take one step after another out into the dark. My shoes make sticking sounds as they find hidden saucers of water. But I don't hear them. The bottoms of my trousers are now flapping in the breeze. But I don't hear them. Even as I move further out into the open I can feel the wall behind, brushing against my back, pushing me forward and out across the square. If I try to slow down I am pushed forward again. If I stop, I still move forward. The square must be moving in on me. The sides are squeezing inwards and the opposite end is moving towards me. I look up at the silhouette of roof tops, to see which way they are moving, but just then, they stop. I look away and then quickly back up again. Still, they are motionless. I turn once more towards the opposite end and see it's great black shadow waiting, obediently as ever, at it's correct distance. Nothing has moved at all, except for me, and even the wall behind is no longer rubbing against my back. Only the rain encircling me disturbs the stillness as the buildings settle once again into rigid attention, waiting once again for my inspection.

I lift my head and, proud with all that I command, I move confidently once more across the square. There is no hesitation now, no filtering steps or shadows in my way. I move freely and quickly charged with a wonderful sense of purpose. I don't even feel the rain which now blows stronger than ever around the silence of the town.

HE FONDLED his empty mug awkwardly, aware of the people around him thinking about what he had just said and he couldn't bear to look up and see the faces trying to make him feel ashamed. He eased himself upright and walked towards the counter with as much dignity as was possible. One of the younger men watched him intently and as he passed by he leaned back and said in a quiet, deliberate voice, 'You know bloody well he was old enough.' The old man said nothing and moved silently on to the counter and pushed his empty mug across the bar.

'I think he was simply a coward,' continued the younger man who by now had turned and was staring at the old man's back. All the more reason to fail, mused the man to himself. But he said nothing. The evenings weren't meant to go like that. Nobody really wanted answers. They didn't all come every time to be reassured by simple explanations or even to solve mysteries, but merely to share a common discomfort when things went wrong. It was part of the ritual of such evenings to keep the clever answers to oneself.

'Why was he chosen anyway?' came a voice from another table.

'He volunteered.'

'We're all volunteers. Why him? Who chose him?'

The room fell silent again. The names of group commanders were sacred names and were never mentioned. They never came to meetings and when they appeared in public it was the rule to pretend one didn't know them. Next to God they were the ones one never questioned. They had to be trusted each time, for better or worse. The men eyed one another knowingly and the question went unanswered. The mystery of the boy was what mattered.

I AM half-way across the square now. With each new step the building opposite leans one way and then the other as it comes forward to meet me. Nothing is holding me back now and as I get nearer, the houses either side of me bow and fold away, respectfully leaving me alone to confront the monolith which heaves itself upright, trying to dwarf me into submission. I stop just short and stand still; waiting for the giant shape to lurch and come crashing down on top of me. I stand upright and dignified expecting to be buried alive and forgotten at once by the houses around the square. But nothing moves. Even my trouser legs stop flapping. But I do not notice. I move forward again and see this time the building doesn't move, but stands dejected and defeated, helplessly betraying whatever lies inside. Pinned down and waiting to be plundered, it is finally at my mercy. I feel the wooden door and realise I am there. It is locked, but I have a key. I could climb up to an open window or force a way in through a side door. But they gave me a key. I take a breath and push the key into the lock and twist it quickly once. I feel the bolt pull silently back and hold, and I let out a mouth full of air. I push against the door and unamazed I watch it swing away from me and into the house. I reach to catch it and as I hold it find I am standing in a large marble hallway. I close the door behind me and lean back against the wood. It clicks shut, but I do not hear it. I feel the wooden frame pressing against my back, holding me upright. I stare straight ahead to see what I have invaded. A long marble hall confronts me and from the end of a pool of light falls in through half closed curtains revealing shadows or furniture and blackened doorways. Everything is still. I grow accustomed to the dimness and count the doors along the wall to my right. There are four. Is there life behind any of them? Which room holds the guards? I look to my left and half way down I see the main stairs. The famous wide stairway they told me about, upon which even the fools of government trembled when ordered up. Going up left and then sharp right at an improbable angle they seemed to support the entire structure of the second floor while at the same time floating between the two levels. They told me about the stairs and told me I would have to climb them. All three of them slept upstairs, they said. Each with his own room. Three room I would have to enter. I look once more to the right and wonder if anyone is awake.

'PERHAPS HE was startled,' said a worried-looking man

leaning sideways across the counter who pulled at his chin in dismay. 'Even seen by one of the guards and chased out of the building.'

'He got further than that.'

'Yes, but. Maybe . . .'

'Maybe nothing. He was there, in the rooms. Each one was there in bed, asleep, and at his mercy. He could have taken all night doing it and robbed the family vault if he felt like it and got away unseen and gone back and done it all over again. He was not interrupted. He had the whole night to himself.' And with that the man banged his fist down on the table and as if mesmerised by his own violence repeated his last remark over and over again. Around the room heads nodded silently in agreement and even the man at the counter was forced to murmer how strange it all seemed. He looked up at the barmaid seeking a kinder face to whom he could explain himself.

'That must have been what got him. You tend to do a lot of thinking when you've got time on your hands. Especially too much time.' Marianne tried to look sympathetic but said nothing. It was never her place to interfere when they all gathered together like this.

Around the room the murmurings settled down into separate discussions at each table. Men who hadn't dared voice their opinions out loud began slowly to exchange ideas with the people sitting next to them.

'I would have been in and out in ten minutes,' boasted one man coldly. 'The quicker the better on missions like that. How was he meant to have done it anyway?'

'With a knife.'

'A knife? That's not the weapon to give a coward to use.'

'Anything else was out of the question.'

'With a knife it is not easy. I have used one myself many times, but it was never easy. It takes more than just strength.'

'I know. But he was trained to use one. He knew what he had to do.'

'Had he ever killed before?'

'Yes. But only with explosives.'

'Just with bombs?'

'Maybe he has shot a few people. I don't know. He's been on missions, though. He's been a few times with me. He looked strong enough then.'

'Anyone can throw a bomb,' said the man, trying hard to restrain his exasperation. To him, throwing a bomb seemed to require nothing more than a sense of direction. A child could do it.

'If I had thought that he wasn't up to any part of it he would not have gone further than one foot with me. Not even out of the door.' They took his word for it and after shrugging helplessly at one another, turned to catch what was being said at the table behind them.

I HEAR no sound from anywhere and turn again to look at the stairs. I count the number of paces it must take me to reach them. Ten at least. I try to steady myself, to build up courage for the approach. But a compulsive urge pulls me from the doors suddenly, and I lunge senselessly across the hallway, reaching out for the marble pillar. I cling to its shape and try hard to stop breathing. I expect lights to go on and doors to crash open, and cold-eyed soldiers walk towards me, surrounding me in triumph. Nothing moves. I pull myself around the pillar and with three large leaps reach the half-landing. I crouch in the corner and force my breathing to quieten down. They must have heard my pounding heart by now. I look up at the final climb and see clearly for the first time the upper landing. It spreads in front of me from left to right just as they told me. They all sleep on this floor, they said. You will not have to move far. You will have to do no searching, they said. I move forward and up a few steps to get a better view of the landing. It is exactly as I have seen it a hundred times. I know each doorway by heart and have measured the paces in between; I have felt the texture of the wood and have seen the view beyond, behind each door. I have felt my way around the darkened floor and touched the table and chairs I knew were there and have gone through the motions of an act that I was trained to do not once, or twice, but a hundred times at least, and maybe more. 'From now on it will be easy, they said. You will not have to think. You will not have to worry. It will all be familiar. It will be just another training exercise. You will want to do better than last time. And even better than the time before that. You are trained to fulfil a task. You will not want to fail. You will want to succeed. There will be no complications. It will be easy. That is what training

is for. You will not even want to think. You will simply act.'
I move up the few remaining steps and stand firmly on the
landing. It is familiar. But this time it gives me no reassurance.
Instead I feel uneasy in front of what I have seen before. I
convince myself that I am seeing it all for the first time.
Suddenly, my training is forgotten.

AT THE table behind the talk was going to and fro in much
the same way. Always one man would begin the exchange
by making some equivocal remark which betrayed no particular sympathies one way or the other, but which served to
rouse the others to enough anger to speak out. Even the older
men present who had grown accustomed to the fact that
every now and again missions failed, and who usually sat
back sage-like nodding at the inevitability of it all, were not
spared the probing questions that flashed back and forth
around the room. It was an occasion for everyone to feel
involved.

'If he had gone one of them it would have been all right.
If he had got the girl even.'

'One was not enough. He should have had them all.'

'But if he had got the girl there would have been no
accession, and without an heir they would have fallen sooner
or later.'

'Sooner or later will not stop the misery that goes on in
the meantime. He should have had them all then. In one go
he could have put a stop to everything.' He looked around
the table, pleased with the way he had suggested hope for a
second and then snatched it back, leaving them to feel even
more bitter and betrayed. It was part of the trick in having
discussions on evenings like this. There was always twice as
much to suffer when things went badly wrong.

'There would have been reprisals, of course,' said a man
sitting slightly away from the table and looking melancholic
at the idea. 'Perhaps me, perhaps my wife; your wife, or your
son. Things wouldn't have come to a halt suddenly.' The
group around him fell silent, each pretending he had not
heard the comment. It was the one point of view they could
never acknowledge; the one consequence of their work they
never talked about. The sad-faced man on his bench knew
this, but he only mentioned it to make the boy's behaviour
all the more inexcusable. 'Perhaps that's what went through

his mind at the last minute. Right there, over their bodies, with the knife in his hands he probably stopped and thought, "Is it worth the risk of losing many friends just for this ?!" ' He paused to allow the possibility of this idea to sink in, watching each for their different reactions. None of them would ever agree to see it that way, but that was obviously the difference between them and the boy. 'If he did think that way then he should never have joined up with us. He was wrong from the start. It should have been spotted at once. And that's our job. We should have seen it early on. We're to blame, really.'

'But he failed, and we suffered just the same anyway. The pity is that it might all have been worth suffering for. The reprisals, I mean.'

I TURN to my left and see the door to the old man's bedroom. What if he isn't there tonight? What if he isn't alone? Maybe these days he can't sleep, and instead lies awake with his eyes open, staring up, and with a loaded gun beside his hand. Waiting for someone he has been expecting for years. Lying guiltily, ready for a night like this. He might even know my name. Straight in front of me I see two doors. Empty rooms they told me. And to the right of them two other doors. One his wife's bedroom, and the other his daughter's. But which is which, and what if they are both awake? Do I look them in the eye and walk towards them, watching their eyes widen in terror, seeing their mouth begin to open and trying to scream, and keep on walking forward till I carry out my deed? Will I have to focus on their upturned faces as I lean forward and create a sudden pain, holding the knife steady till I am sure the recoiling body has subsided and sunk back forever, never to move again? Then retreat, move on a room, and do it once again. And finally turn again into another room, and do it yet once more. That is what they trained me for. That is what they expect of me. 'Get the old man first,' they said. 'If things go wrong make sure you get him at least. Leave the others, but get him. You might only have time for one.' Their words come back to me but their voices sound far off now. I start to turn to my left to face the left-hand room but something checks me, and instead I swivel round and move towards the other rooms. Past the empty rooms, past the third door, until

I am standing outside the bedroom door that I must enter first. The daughter's room, I hope. I pray she is asleep. I am not breathing now as I turn the handle slowly and push. The door floats slowly away from me. The interior opens up in front of me and suddenly I know for certain I have been here before. Memory takes over and without thinking I close the door and start to glide towards the bed, missing chairs and tables I do not even see. I make for the chair I know is beside the bed and see the still form I know to be asleep; asleep then, and asleep now. I sit down and look up at the daughter's face turned slightly towards me as it always was, half hidden by the fold in the pillow, but peaceful and silent, with eyes closed. She doesn't move. I stare at her face and try hard to remember what it is she has done or what she represents, or why she is my enemy. I stare hard and long and wrestle with the list of her crimes, going over and over the many accusations that I have been through many times before. I begin to tremble. This much I have been through. I have rehearsed it and rehearsed it, but now there is something new. Something I must do for the first time. Everything else is familiar; that is training. Now I must create a new sensation. Something which will give this familiarity a new dimension. A single simple act which will rid me of the routine that I have been through again and again. I start to tremble even more and my hands are shaking in a way I have never seen them before. I lift one hand and reach for the knife but it resists half way. I try to concentrate and force it inside my jacket but it will not move. My whole body is shaking now and I look up to see if she has woken, but she is still asleep. She was then, and is now. I look down at my hand and see it shaking pathetically, unable to move that bit more to grab the knife. I stare at it, bewildered, remembering how it went the many times in training. It must be simple. But my hand will not move. I look up once more at the sleeping face and realise that I cannot do it. I could not do it then, and I cannot do it now. I have reached this penultimate stage a hundred times, but now, confronted, I cannot take it one act beyond. I am unprepared. I rise out of my chair and clumsily thread my way past pieces of furniture towards the door. My hands still shaking, I struggle to open it quietly. Eventually it opens and I squeeze out into the corridor and shut it behind me. When I heard it click I lean back and breath in deeply, trying to stop the shaking.

'OBVIOUSLY, we must be more careful with our choices in future,' said one of the men. 'Such opportunities do not present themselves so often. A bad decision like that cannot happen again. We would all be rounded up in no time.' He spoke quietly as if to give some rationality to their shared frustrations, and his voice carried with it an air of authority. 'That is the first lesson we must take from this whole affair. Perhaps it will be a good thing in the long run to re-examine all the people who work with us.'

'And the boy? What of him?'

'He will not show himself too readily for some time yet. In fact, I hear he has gone to ground.' He looked around him, half expecting someone to make an angry comment at this piece of news. But no one said a word. It was as if they had all grown tired of being angry anymore.

'No, gentlemen, whether in success or in failure, we must all share the responsibility. Otherwise as a cause we make no sense.' He lifted his jug in a mock toast, but when he saw no one joining in, he gave a disapproving shrug and then drank it anyway. He waved the empty jug above his head and called for Marianne to bring him another one. Around him people started to chatter in small groups again. But this time no one seemed to be listening very hard. Mainly because they were talking about other things. Over by the wall, however, two of them hadn't given up.

'Things aren't so hopeless really. Looking at it one way, there will always be other chances, whatever people say. Perhaps you and I will get a chance to do it properly next time.'

I PRESS my hands against the door behind me, spreading them and pushing hard, waiting for each finger to settle down while I continue to take in deep gulps of air. I turn my head to the right and see the door to the second bedroom just a few feet away. I move towards it, pressing close against the wall as I inch along. I stand outside it and tell myself that it will be better this time. It must be all right this time. I pull away from the wall and stand boldly in front of the door, steadying myself for another act of strength. Staring at the handle I tell myself it is routine and that I have done it once successfully before. That I have met the crisis once, and I handled it. But as soon as I start to remember what lies behind the door, and how the room is arranged and who lies there, and what it is I have to do, I feel myself trembling again. And I know I haven't done it once already, and I know that there is something new behind the door, inside the room I know so well, something I will not be able to face. I will meet it once again for the first time and I know I will give in. It's a lie that I will handle it. And it's a lie that I have been trained to go through with it. I cannot go through the door, into a room I have been in a hundred times, and be unable to carry out my task. I cannot. I spring sideways and press my back against the wall again, and hear the sound of my frantic breathing rising and falling, now louder than ever. I look across at the stairs and then along to the third bedroom door, and then back at the stairs again. I begin to lose all feeling of certainty. I cannot even think what to do. I could simply run. But I cannot move. Then I hear the voices again. 'If things go wrong, get the old man at least. Leave the others, but get him at least. Get him at least.' I look at the door and see the shadow of it's arch yawning at me, mocking me, as I try to hide against the dimness of the wall. Silently teasing me to come forward, I stare at it, watching the yawn grow. Suddenly, I push away and start running towards it. I pull up short and see from this angle that the smile is gone. I take one deep breath and push open the door. I know the room well. I do not have to stop to locate anything. I move quickly, straight for the bed. He is there as I remember, asleep and at my mercy. I look down at him and try not to think about the history of his actions or anything about him. I see a victim, lying face down with his head turned away from me. I reach for my knife and grab it firmly in my hand. The handle fits tightly in my palm. I hold it up and raise my arm high above the sleeping form. He still doesn't move. I start to bring my arm down in a full arc but I stop half way. I feel the shaking coming on again and I lift my arm back up to it's full height. My hand is shaking wildly now but I tell myself that one sudden thrust will cure it forever. The shaking gets out of control and the weight of my upraised arm begins to get heavier and heavier. It is now a huge weight and the handle of the knife is burning into my palm, stinging the skin which feels red hot with pain.

I try to twist my fingers around, but even they are an enormous weight now. Stuck together, they will not unwind. They are welded to the knife which now dances about above me. I look up and see my whole arm swaying about, pivoting from my elbow. I pretend it will stop any minute, but I know it won't. I pretend that I have gone through with it, but I know I haven't. I lift up my other arm to try and steady the shaking. Now both arms are swaying about and the combined weight becomes unbearable. I know that I am not going to do it. I summon up last efforts of energy, and still I know that I am not going to do it. I let my arms fall down and swing helplessly either side of me. I hear low moans begin to come from my mouth. I cannot control them, and I feel my body aching all over. I feel tired. Exhausted. I turn away from the bed and walk unconsciously towards the door. I lean against the wall, trying hard to stay upright. I lift my hand to look at the clean, unused knife, and notice that the knuckles have almost broken through the skin. The whole hand is white and glows in the darkness all around me. Suddenly, the sound of a door slamming cracks through the silence. I straightened involuntarily. There are sounds of foot steps and then another door shutting. I move out onto the landing and listen for further sounds. It is silent again everywhere. Quickly, without thinking, I swing round the pillar and start running down the stairs. I reach the half landing in three leaps and then turn to jump the few remaining steps. I reach the marble hall and make for the front door. Just then, a door opposite opens and a young soldier walks out holding a pile of notes. He looks up and stops when he sees me. I stop and look back at him. For seconds we stand there, looking at each other, saying nothing. His mouth is half open, paralysed with disbelief at what he sees. Then he shouts. I do not hear him. I turn and run for the front door. More shouting starts. But I do not hear it. I am running out into the square across the cobbled stones, running with a freedom I have longed for. All the frightened muscles that were tensed into knots suddenly unwind and every part of me starts to move freely. Lights are going on and windows opening all around the square, but I do not see them. I only feel the wonderful comfort of the cobbles passing under foot as I breath in the gallons of fresh air that swirl about me. There are soldiers chasing me, but I swing my arms around and keep on running towards the side street on the far side. Tomorrow I will face my comrades and there will be questions and answers. Some will hate me, some will never forgive me, and others will just pity me. But some will understand. Tomorrow, though. Tomorrow they can have me and all the answers they want to know. But tonight I am innocent and free. They will not catch me. Not even the screaming soldiers behind me, running across the square.

THE TWO men arguing in the corner were just about to reach a compromise when the door crashed open suddenly. It swung fully open and bounced against the wall, settling to a steady knock. For a while no one came in and there was only the sound of the wind outside competing with the noise of the pounding rain which poured down on the streets. But no one moved or even turned around. Finally, a figure came up the steps and stood in the doorway, silently looking in. The room went quiet, but still no one turned and looked. They didn't need to. It was the head of security police and they always knew when it was he who had arrived. He scanned the room with a serious look and then, as if not fully satisfied, he moved a few paces into the room and then shut the door. He lifted his cap off carefully, and then held it slightly away from him. He tipped it gently at an angle and watched a little stream of water hit the floor. He looked down at the semi-circle of damp that covered the doorway. He examined the patch intently, trying to distinguish foot prints in the mess. He moved slightly in one direction hoping to find a single set of prints leading off somewhere. But the dampness seemed to spread everywhere and he could distinguish nothing. He smiled to himself as if remembering some private joke. He stood upright and walked towards the tables where he proceeded to move up and down between the different groups, examining their faces as he went. They were unfriendly as ever, but he had grown used to that. It was right that they should hate him, of course, but it was still amusing somehow to watch them feign indifference to his presence, as if the power he had made no difference to them. It gave him all the more pleasure in teasing them with his conversation.

'So much rain, and yet so many people out of their homes,' he said, looking around at them all. They turned away pretending not to notice. 'Or is there a celebration going on?' Again, no one stirred. They didn't even start to talk to one another which was one way they had of making him feel an unwanted intruder. They just stared silently into their mugs waiting for him to leave. Finally, he put his cap back on and marched towards the door. He put his hand on the handle and as an afterthought turned to look back at the sorry group of men around the tables.

'Be careful when you go home tonight. Stick to the main streets and stay in the open where possible. I have doubled the patrols tonight and with all this rain visibility can be confusing. I wouldn't want there to be any accidents. It would be terrible to have someone shot for nothing.' He stood there for a while waiting to make sure his warning had been heard. Then he opened the door and went out into the night.

The room remained silent with no one quite sure what to say next. Marianne put down an empty jug and from behind her counter looked across at the dejected faces that filled her tavern. Her eyes moved from face to face, marvelling at the uniformity of their expressions. She had seen it all many times before but it didn't stop her suffering a little with them each time.

'It's time to go home. It's getting late and there's nothing more to be said tonight.'

But no one heard her, and no one moved.

BERYL BAINBRIDGE
Eric on the Agenda

MY CHILDHOOD friend rang at twelve o'clock. She said she was very well and that she had met such a nice man on the train up to Scotland and she had given him my address. She hoped it was alright. I hadn't seen my friend for at least ten years so I couldn't tell her she was rotten for giving my name to a perfect stranger.

'Of course it's alright, Anthea,' I said. 'And how are all the children?'

'He's a bit fat,' said my friend. 'But you were never superficial.'

'What's his name?'

'Eric. He wears a trilby hat . . . I thought at the time you and he had a lot in common.'

At two o'clock the taxi arrived with my Mum. She stood on the pavement, nylon wig motionless, fox fur quivering in the sunlight. She laughed shrilly like some animal caught in a trap when I embraced her. I touched her frozen curls and buried my mouth in the soft fur at her neck. How we hugged each other, how we began sentences and never finished them, what a noise she made; how she teetered between the cracks in the flagstones of the tiny garden. She had painted her nails scarlet and she wore her serpent brooch and her pearls and her second best watch. I carried her two suitcases inside and left them in the hall alongside the hat box in which she kept her Joyce Grenfell wig.

'Don't leave my cases there, dear,' she said. 'If you don't mind.'

She was still laughing on that high prolonged note of joy, waving her plump little hands about, and I dragged her luggage into the front room where she could keep an eye on it. I knew what was in the cases. Three or four cocktail dresses and a ball gown or two. Shoes to match. Also bunches of cloth flowers, roses, and purple pansies with limp stitched leaves, a little gold safety pin at the back, ready to adorn her waist or breast or shoulder strap. The dresses – the midnight blue silk, the green satin with diamanté bodice – would hang reproachfully from the picture rail in my living room, until it was time to pack them again. The sight of them filled me with despair, flaring out from the wall whenever I opened the door too quickly; the rustle of taffeta, the whisper of silk. When I switched on the electric light the glory of the bodice blinded me.

She never asked if we were going to any Balls. She just hoped. She never asked if I minded her taking my bed. She just assumed. She hid her teeth and her diamond rings under the pillow at night. She put her wig over my statue of a lady patting a dog. Once, a long time ago, Alice my youngest had gone in to see her early in the morning. She had tugged at the bed-clothes and asked – 'Are you the cleaning lady?' I don't know where she got the idea from. We had never had a cleaning lady, certainly not one that slept on the premises, and my Mum said Alice took after me. During that same visit she offered to buy me a wig. She said I would look a blooming sight better without those rat-tails falling about my ears. I said I couldn't bear it – what happened if somebody stroked your head and it all slipped sideways? – and she said, you mean *men* . . . you're no better than a prostitute, and I said I never got any money for it. But that was some years past and I treated her better now, more like a parent to a child.

'Anything on the agenda for this evening?' she asked, sitting down at the table.

I pretended I hadn't heard. Instead I said 'I've got those choccy biccies you like.'

She said, 'Goody, goody.'

Whilst I was pouring the tea the phone rang and I answered it without thinking. It was Eric. He said he was in London for twenty-four hours and he would call round quite soon if I had no objection. I knew my Mum was listening so I couldn't say no, you can't, my Mother is here, because she would think it was someone vital and interesting asking me to a Ball and I was putting them off on account of being ashamed of her who had given me birth. So I said 'Yes do, thank you.'

'I'll bring a drop of the you know what,' he said.

'Who was that?' asked my Mum.

'A friend of Anthea's.'

'Anthea who?' She was looking at me hungrily, searching my mouth as if she was deaf and needed to lip read. Just at the edge of her powdered chin was a smear of chocolate.

'Anthea Wilson . . . you know . . . down the lane.'

'Anthea Wilson. My word! Her grandmother is still alive you know . . . still popping up and down in the lift at the

Bon Marché.'

'Is she ?' I said. 'What about Uncle Teddy ?'

'Uncle who ?'

'The one with the boating blazer.'

'What boating blazer ?'

'You've got choccy on your chin.'

She took out a handkerchief and rubbed her mouth. I stared at her. The light went out of her eyes. 'There never was an Uncle Teddy,' she said.

She never noticed the new curtains or the fact that the floor had been polished. She stared out of the window at the newly planted fox-gloves by the bins and said the weeds were getting out of hand. She didn't comment on the clean table-cloth. She did spot immediately that the stairs looked bare. She was like a trained athlete when the starting flag begins to dip – she was off in a flash, mouth drooping in disappoint-ment, head a little to one side as she contemplated the naked wood.

'What happened to your stair carpet ?'

'I lent it to Edith. I'm getting it back.'

'I see.' She pulled herself up by the banister rail, a little bundle of fur and false curls, shrunken now the re-union was over, and as always, not up to expectation.

The man in the trilby hat came at four o clock. He was awful. He was shaped like a pear drop and his coat wouldn't fasten and he wore spectacles and woolly gloves. He was holding a big cardboard box in his arms.

'I've brought the you know what,' he said. I don't think he liked me either. He was a bit like my Mum, the way his glance slid away from my face – you could almost see the dream of fair women fading from the dull green glass of his eyes. He was more her age than mine, the same vulnerable generation, quite incapable of disguising disappointment. You'd have thought with all that experience of hunger marches and depression and inhibition, they'd be twice as good at not showing their feelings; but there he stood, face quivering like a neglected baby, eyelids trembling as if to stop tears, just like my Mother over me lending the stair-carpet to Edith. I couldn't think what Anthea had told him. When we were little she had been the pretty one, sort of Shirley Temple whilst I was sort of Margaret O'Brien. Then later on I thought I got better looking and she went on

wearing ankle socks and her heeled shoes with her slacks.
But that was ten years ago – and standards are different in
London. My Mother thinks I look awful too.

'Oh hallow,' she cried perking up as Eric came into the
kitchen with his cardboard box. She gave one of her social
laughs and tossed her curls about. You could tell Eric was
surprised to find a Mother in the house.

'I can see,' he said, 'that it's not convenient at the moment.
I'll call back later.'

'Oh you'll call again, will you?' she trilled. He put down
on the table his box full of the you know what. He said he
would return at nine o clock when things were settled and I
was more myself.

'He seemed rather nice,' said my Mother. She felt inside
the carton with inquisitive fingers. 'What's he returning for?'

'It's business,' I told her. 'Something to do with Anthea.'

She was lifting out a bottle of whisky. 'Is he a traveller,'
she asked, 'for Johnny Walker?'

'I think he's Anthea's accountant.'

There were three bottles of whisky, three of gin, and what
my Mum called the equipment – dry gingers and bitter lemon.

'Rum sort of accountant,' she said, 'bringing all drink.'

'What's he mean about me being more myself?' I worried.
'I'm me now.'

'He probably meant when things were tidier,' she reasoned,
but she was smiling as if the evening promised well for us
all. It made me very sad. Sad that Eric on the agenda gave
her cause for excitement, sad for Eric that hadn't been what
he expected, and resentful at both of them for being de-
pendant on me.

'Things,' I cried, 'are very tidy. And I'm not asking Edith
for the staircarpet back just for that silly old turd in a trilby
hat.' I don't think she knew what the word meant. She said
he had raised his hat to her when he came in. In the end I
went round to see Edith and told her to pop in about nine
for a drink.

'It's desperate,' I said. 'This awful man thinks there's
going to be an orgy.' Edith offered to phone Lily. She said
Lily was jolly useful at that sort of thing.

My Mother got dressed up at about eight o clock. Not
exactly a cocktail gown, but practically – off the shoulder
brocade and shoes to match. She played several rounds of

gin rummy with the children. She couldn't bear to lose at cards. She added up her score triumphantly and squirmed on her chair with satisfaction, writing down the total with her gold pencil with the tassel. 'I've won, I've won,' she cried, radiant with laughter. The children said nothing.

I put on a clean jumper and really tried with my hair, back combing it and spraying it to stay in place. 'Do make yourself presentable,' said my Mother when I had finished.

Edith behaved beautifully to her. Gentle and complimentary – almost flirtatious – fingering her earrings and saying how pretty they were and admiring the winkle-picker shoes. 'You look younger than ever,' she cried, and my Mum never mentioned she missing staircarpet. They both wanted to start on the drink at once but I wouldn't let them. I went to the pub and bought a half bottle of whisky to keep them cheerful. They thought I was mad not touching Eric's cardboard box.

'If he wants to bloody well waste your time coming here, he ought to provide the booze,' said Edith, looking at me with contempt. My Mother never noticed if other people swore.

'I don't want to be beholden to the bloody man,' I protested.

'Wash your mouth out,' said my Mum.

I couldn't sit still, I was so bothered about what Eric expected. I kept thinking of him in his woolly gloves sitting opposite Anthea on the train up to Scotland. She'd probably told him she had an arty friend in London who was divorced and very friendly and who loved a drop of the you know what. It was all based on her knowledge of me when I was fourteen, when she and I had gone to the cinema to see Stewart Granger in 'Caravan' and I had got off with a soldier from Harrington Barracks. 'Rita Moody,' Anthea had whined, corkscrew ringlets quivering with agitation, 'just you dare go off with that soldier.' And I said it was none of her business and she'd followed me to the Park and seen me go into the bowls pavilion with the soldier and a bottle of sparkling Vimto. She confessed she had listened to the noises we made – she even wrote it down in her diary and put my name in it. I never spoke to her again until we were grown up.

When Eric came he was smelling of after-shave and he

had changed his tie.

'Good God,' said Edith. 'So you're Eric.'

He was terribly nonplussed at seeing the two women at the table. He huffed up and down the kitchen with his feet splayed out and he gave them a whole bottle of whisky to add to the half-bottle, and some of the 'equipment'. My Mum kept digging Edith in the ribs, and Edith kept rolling her eyes.

'We'll just go upstairs,' I said, 'and talk a bit of business.' It was a foolish thing to say but I couldn't spend the whole evening in the kitchen and not explain that there had been some mistake.

He did notice the lack of stair carpet. 'Spot of decorating?' he said. He thought my living room, once it had been re-organised and decorated, would be very nice. I had spent two years getting my living room as I wanted it, though the ball gowns hanging from the rail obscured the pictures and the photographs. We sat on my green sofa. It was worth an awful lot of money though the springs were lax and he wasn't doing them any good. We talked about him meeting Anthea on the train.

'Lovely girl,' he said.

'Look,' I began, 'I think there's been some mistake.'

'I found her very simpatico . . . if you follow me.'

'Her grandmother,' I said, 'is still alive. And her Uncle Teddy.'

He said 'May I make a bold suggestion?' and I thought how I would write Anthea a very cool letter just as soon as I had a moment. He said if I would turn the light off it would make him feel more peaceful, so I did, because I thought it would be easier to tell him where to get off, if I couldn't see his face. I had my legs crossed under my long black skirt and a pair of tights and some Greek sandals. I couldn't really keep the sandals on with stockings, but I tried, and suddenly he caught hold of my ankle.

'May I,' he said, 'ask you something personal?'

'There may have been,' I said, 'a misunderstanding.'

'I just want to hold your big toe.'

I didn't know what to do. 'I'm not taking my sock off,' I said weakly. So we sat there in the darkness and he stroked my big toe. After a while he confided.

'I'm very much in favour of going into Europe, though I'm

not in favour of a Labour government.' He sounded very peaceful, almost sleepy.

'I must pop down and see if my Mum is alright,' I said. She and Edith had almost finished the large bottle of whisky. My Mum looked pretty and gay and unresentful. Had she been alone and without a drink she would have long since created a scene and called me a loose woman.

'Do you know,' I said, 'he's been fiddling with my big toe.' And we all clutched our stomachs and bellowed with mirth.

'Darling,' said Edith, 'it can be very enjoyable . . . no, don't laugh' . . . and I looked from her to my little Mum and back again and my mouth stretched wide open and for some reason I thought about the chocolate covered coon man, singing about his silvery moon in the sky, and how once when I was small my Mum had wheeled me on a bicycle when I had been fetched home from school with a stomach ache.

'Do you remember', I said, 'how you held me on that bicycle' – but she didn't, she had no recollection. She started saying – 'what bicycle, what coon, what are you on about ?' – and I went back upstairs to Eric. He wanted to know when they were going home.

'They're not,' I said. 'They live here.'

I sat on a chair on the other side of the room.

'Do you know,' he said, out of the darkness, 'I could guarantee that if we lay down anywhere I would not be capable of doing you know what.'

'Well,' I said, 'now you mention it, I can guarantee I wouldn't lie down.' And we both sat silent, listening to the dresses whispering on the wall.

'Rita . . . Rita' . . . called my Mother. He said he better be going back to his hotel. It had been very nice meeting me.

'I don't approve of the Common Market,' I told him, as he went noisily downstairs. 'And you shouldn't mess about with people's feet.'

He shook hands with my Mother and with Edith. Though she was hostile you could tell he wished Anthea had given him her address instead of mine. We all watched to see if he would take his cardboard box with him. He moved towards it but Edith looked at him so brutally that he faltered and said he would call for it another time. I wouldn't go to the door with him. I pretended I felt sick.

My Mum and Edith talked for hours. Edith fetched a bottle of gin from Eric's box and they began on that. I couldn't go to sleep because my Mother had my bed and I was supposed to sleep on the sofa. I didn't have any extra blankets and I didn't want her to know how uncomfortable I was when she came to stay. I put on my old fur coat and lay down. She was telling Edith how strange I was. How I'd always been awkward, even as a child.

'That business about the bicycle,' she said. 'I don't know what she's on about. We never had a bicycle. My husband –'

– 'my Dad,' I said.

' . . . never had a bicycle. My son never had –'

– 'my brother,' I told her, but she wasn't listening.

The room was turning round. I could hear the music. There was Edith with her dark head circling above the table-cloth, and my little Mum, shoulders dipping and her pearls like a string of stars as she flew with outstretched arms, skirts whirling, in a great circle about the ballroom.

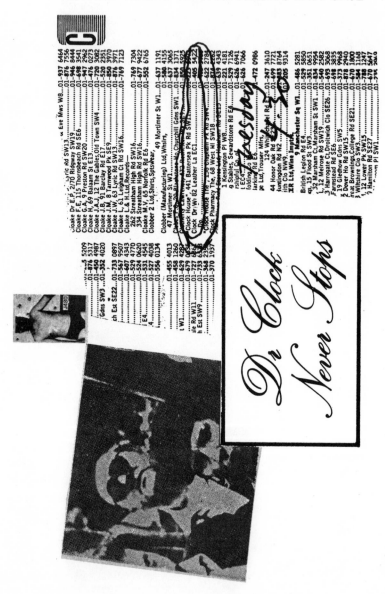

'DR CLOCK, CURES ALL ILLS', it said on the card he gave her as soon as she was inside the room, and she put it in the side pocket of her handbag and believed him.

'Come to bed with me,' he said, 'and I'll make you better.' He began to undo the jacket of his greasy suit and his trouser buttons, long-haired grey head bent down, grunting slightly as he strained over his paunch to reach them, as if never doubting for one moment that she would do whatever he ordered.

It wasn't really a bed, but a couch upholstered in the same faded blue woven stuff that covered its three pillows, standing against one wall of what he referred to as his consulting chamber. A tall narrow window, blurred by the dirt of years, opened onto a courtyard at the back of the building, and that afternoon the room was made even darker by rain falling from an overcast, grey sky.

Lucy still wore her coat – a military style black mackintosh. She hesitated in the centre of the room, a slight, fair woman of about thirty, watching him undress but not able to make a move herself. She felt satisfied but tired, as though at last she had arrived at the place she had been seeking of so long. Everything she wore today was black or some other muted, sombre shade, except for her underpants, which were a vivid purple that glowed like neon.

'Come on now, get your clothes off. Put that handbag down. You look like a prison visitor.' Dr Clock, shapely fat knees and calves revealed between high socks and longish cotton shorts of green and white stripes, tutted impatiently. 'You want me to cure you, don't you? Well, let's get on with it.'

'Can you really cure all ills?' she asked wonderingly, twisting around to unzip her skirt. It all seemed so easy and matter of fact once she began that it was obvious he could. Otherwise, why would she be here?

'Headache, heartache, hernia, haemorrhoids, hopelessness, or any other list you could make. Just you get undressed and believe what I tell you.' Dr. Clock was naked now, but seemed exactly the same as when he'd opened the door fully clothed. His compact body, like a rubber doll's, appeared warm and healthy and entirely unselfconscious. 'You'll feel cold, I suppose,' he muttered and stooped to light the gas-fire. 'I like that purple, let's put them over the lamp.' He

187

reached out for the nylon pants and draped them over the shade of his desk light, and the room became a grotto. 'Now come over here and sit next to me.' He seated himself on the couch and patted the padded surface. 'Tell me what's the matter.'

Except for the first sight of him when he had opened the door, there hadn't really been a chance to examine his face. An impression of paleness, of profuse greyish hair and rather bulging pale eyes was all Lucy could remember from what had only been a few minutes ago. She was sitting next to him now, but somehow felt so curiosity to twist around and scrutinise him more closely.

'Come on, tell me what's the matter,' he repeated. 'That's why you came here, isn't it? That's why you rang my bell and took my card and read it and put it away somewhere safe. Lie back, and tell me why you came here.'

She stretched out on the rough surface of the couch and he bent over and peered at the middle of her body. 'I saw your advertisement on a notice-board, so I just came here and hoped you'd see me,' she began. 'Yes, yes,' he said soothingly, putting one hand gently onto her belly. 'And why did you think I could help you?' His head was bent so low he seemed to be smelling her, yet she was sure he was listening intently. 'I need someone to help me. Something is wrong with me, I know that.'

The heat from the gas-fire and its flickering light on the purpled ceiling made her feel drowsy and relaxed. It seemed years since she'd been so comfortable. 'Open your legs,' Dr Clock said. 'I want you to talk to me, because I know that's what you want to do. You don't want to listen to me. I don't have to say anything. You know what's the matter.' Complying was confirmation of his diagnosis. Of course she knew what was the matter with her and what she wanted. Her hip joints rolled her flexed legs easily outwards as he bent even lower and fastened his mouth around the parted lips of her vagina and began a soft regular pumping sucking like a baby at the nipple.

'I thought something was wrong with me when I was out there,' Lucy mused, watching the patterns on the walls and ceiling, distanced like all the complexities of her life far away outside in the winter city. 'But in here I think that there's nothing much wrong with me, really, after all. It's just them.' She ended on an interrogatory note, but Dr Clock did not lift his head to answer, and so after a short pause she continued. What he was doing wasn't exciting her in the sense of taking her away from herself. That gentle, rhythmic sucking made her more complete, as though if it could somehow continue and remain with her always, even after she left this room, if she could just take his lips away with her and leave the rest of him behind, then she would be invulnerable to any pain or uncertainty for the rest of her life. 'None of my pains are real,' she said. 'I'm not sick, am I ?' The question didn't even need an answer. The knots in her joints and intestines were loosening like flaccid snakes after coupling. Dr Clock's mouth increased its grip, a hand moved under her hips and tilted her pelvis slightly.

'If I could feel like this all the time then nothing would hurt me, would it ?' Lucy asked. 'All the problems would go away, wouldn't they ?' She vaguely sensed some contradiction to what she had said earlier, but was beginning not to care whether what she said was consistent or not, or even if she went on talking. But Dr Clock obviously would not tolerate silence. He lifted up his head and ordered, 'Go on, you mustn't stop talking. You haven't said anything yet.'

'Leave me alone,' she gasped. 'Stop telling me what to do. Everyone tells me what to do, I can't stand it!' She half pulled herself up, wanting to glare furiously at him, but he firmly, gently, pressed her back until she was lying down again.

'Everyone bullies me,' she sobbed, bucking up and down, in the grip of a tantrum such as she could only dimly remember from early childhood. She tried to pull his restraining arms away from her body, tried to twist herself around to see him. But he kept his grip firm, and she could only scream, 'I hate you, you're always stopped me from doing what I want, you never let me have anything. I hate you. You're like everyone else, they're all against me, no one will do anything for me, I'm all alone!'

The purple light seemed glacial. She was in such desolation, felt such isolation and misery, such raging frustration because he would not let her sink away and forget herself entirely. 'I'm alone, all alone, oh, I'm so unhappy!' Tears of self-pity poured from her eyes and softened her anger. If only he would comfort her she would forgive anything. 'Nobody has ever loved me – never – nobody, and now you're just the same. I thought you'd cure me, but you're only making me even sicker.' It was true. All over her body nodes of pain flared. She was frightened by their clanging, grinding intensity, and by the conviction that she was about to die. 'Oh forgive me,' she pleaded, stretching out her arms. 'I'll do whatever you say if only you'll forgive me and be kind to me. I can't stand it.'

'Get up now,' Dr Clock said. 'I want you to beat me. Here.' He pulled the leather belt from his trousers and handed it to her. 'Hit me. Take it out on me. You don't want me to forgive you at all. It's just that you're too frightened to punish me. Well, hit me.'

'No, no,' she pleaded. 'I do want you to forgive me, really, please. No one has ever forgiven me. I'm a great sinner.'

'All right, then,' he said. 'If you want to be punished, I'll do it for you.'

The first lash shocked, but the next blows infuriated her. 'Give that to me,' she shouted, trying to dodge the strap and wrest it from his hand. 'I do hate you, it's true. I do want to beat you. I want to kill you. I want to kill everyone, because nobody ever forgives me or loves me. Give that strap to me, you bastard.' She still couldn't see what he looked like, blinded by fury, but it didn't matter; he looked like everyone she'd ever known: her father, her grandfathers, her uncles, her grown-up, smirking cousins, every man who'd ever teased and played with and rejected her.

'Hit me,' he said, surrendering the strap. He waited passively half turned away. Lucy lashed out at his back and shoulders, but in that position he looked sexless, neuter, hermaphroditic, more like a plump, comfortable middle-aged woman than a man. She stopped, and frowned, and blinked, shaking the sweat-heavy hair from her eyes. Surely it was her mother standing there? In just that way her mother had stared into the gas-fire at home when Lucy had been a child, halted in her dressing by some reverie. Would it be possible to hit her mother? Did she want to?

'Are you my mother?' she asked in a low nervous, voice. 'Mother?' Whoever it was, the figure did not turn around. For God's sake, tell me if you're my mother,' Lucy pleaded. Why don't you turn around? Don't you love me? Mother –' She fell onto her knees and began to beat her head on the floor. 'Mother, mother, mother,' she moaned. Do I want to hit my mother ?' It was too terrible a dilemma to bear.

'You don't have to hit me it you don't want to,' Dr Clock said. He turned and put a warm arm around her trembling shoulders.

'I can't kill my mother,' Lucy cried. 'It would be suicide.' He led her over to the couch again and lay her down and stroked her, and she immediately fell into an exhausted sleep.

A FEW minutes later she sat up, alert and refreshed.

'Read this,' he said. While she was asleep he must have moved into the armchair where he now sat, cross-legged and pensive, wearing a multi-coloured silk kimono. It was another card, the same sort as the first, but with a different message. 'Dr Clock Never Stops.'

'Say the alphabet for me,' he commanded, while she was still studying the cryptic inscription.

'The alphabet ?' she repeated, confused.

'Yes, come on, begin now, start saying the alphabet.' He wasn't even looking at her, but was twirling a loose thread in the hem of the kimono.

'A . . . A-B-C-' Lucy began, barely able to believe that she was complying with his orders as if she had no will of her own, as if he had hypnotised her. She felt cold and pathetic. 'D-E-F-G-' It was impossible to think about anything else while reciting these letters, saying these words – they took over her entire mind like a meditation exercise. 'H-I-J-K-L-' All she was aware of was the alphabet, and of him controlling her. 'M-N-O-P-Q-R-S-' She felt drawn towards him, impelled to move closer, and still with eyes fixed on the purple-tinged figure glowing down one side from the reflection of the gas-fire hidden behind the bulk of the armchair, crouched slightly to touch the floor with her hands, and slowly began to move forward on all fours. 'T-U-V-W-X-Y-Z.' When she had reached the last letter her face was level with his knees. She sat on the carpet and laid her head in his lap.

Softly, heavily, firmly, he pressed her face down. 'Kiss my cock,' he said, shifting so that he would be more exposed. Lucy closed her eyes and parted her lips, and felt a thick, half-erect penis slide between them. It stiffened and enlarged in her mouth – she moved her tongue around it, swallowed and gulped and gagged as it pressed deeper down into her throat and she began to think she would suffocate. 'Kneel down,' he said, pulling away, when she was already sure she was about to choke and die. He knelt behind her and clasped a breast in each hand.

'Ah!' she groaned at his penetration.

'Now, say the alphabet,' he ordered.

'I can't,' she moaned. 'Leave me alone.'

'Come on, begin.' He emphasised the order by a deep thrust.

'A-B-C-D-' At each letter it seemed that she opened more, perceived herself as more burning and swollen, fluttered and dragged him further inside her. By contrast he barely moved, only to use his penis as a sort of prod when she stopped for too long, or began to droop towards the floor. There was no way to measure the duration of the alphabet. Between some letters it seemed as if she had sunk unto the heart of a mountain of black basalt which would have to be eroded away by time and weather before she would be released to intone the next sound. She had never felt so content, so rested.

'Now stand up,' he said, at 'Z', abruptly drawing back, wrapping the kimono around himself and sitting down again. Dazed and confused, Lucy looked around at the strange room. She could barely remember who or where she was, or why she knelt there, arms stiff and trembling, knees chafed by the rough carpeting. 'Tell me why you came to see me. What do you think I can do for you?'

She tried to draw her consciousness away from the present moment and remember. 'Cure me, that's it,' she said at last. 'I want you to cure me. I want you to stop me from suffering. I want to escape from all the passions that torment me. I want to be able to live.'

'To live?' he repeated.

'Maybe that isn't exactly what I mean, after all,' Lucy amended uncertainly. Things seemed to be getting worse. 'This is living right now, isn't it? But I must find some way to be played on by everything that happens or has ever happened in the past. Sometimes I even think that future events are sending their influences back at me. How can one be less harsh to anyone else that one has been to oneself?

I don't have the temperament for my beliefs.'

'I am not Dr Spock.'

'Who's Dr Spock?' she wondered. 'You're Dr Clock, aren't you?'

'Dr Clock, the lollipop,' he answered gleefully, and leaned forward to put one hand on each side of her head and drag her towards him, clamping her startled, rigid face down into his groin again and roughly pushing his iron penis against her mouth until he had forced it open, then thrusting it down her throat and discharging a thick, hot, copious stream of semen. 'Swallow it,' he commanded sternly. 'It's your first dose of my medicine.'

Her throat convulsed with involuntary gagging, then as the viscous liquid mixed with her own saliva she tried to savour its faint saltiness. 'This is your medicine, is it?' she mumbled abstractedly when she could speak. 'I don't see how it's going to cure me.'

'It's life, my dear lady. You say you want life – that's the essence of life, so I understand. What better medicine could I give you?'

'I don't see that it's any different in here than anywhere else,' Lucy said, petulant and bitter. She stood up, brushed back her disordered hair, and moved over to the gas-fire to lean against the mantlepiece and stare down into the flames. It wasn't the taste in her mouth which was making her feel sick, it was intense disappointment. 'This is the sort of thing that's always happening,' she began, her voice strained and haranguing with the effort to appear reasonable. 'What's the difference between you and everyone else? You've only made me feel worse. I thought there was some hope some-where –' She had to break off, because she was spiralling out of control. No matter how hard she tried the tears wouldn't hold back. She turned entirely away, in an attempt to hide her face, wet as if a sheet of silent water had washed over it. The gas-fire flashed and sparkled through her lashes. But her misery was too overwhelming for silence. She rushed over to the couch and threw herself down onto it, pulled the heavy, square cushions over on top of herself, and howled and roared with grief.

Such an outburst couldn't sustain itself for long against his uninvolvement. 'So I disappointed you, did I, Lucy? But you didn't come to me for gratification did you, but to be cured.'

'But you said I should come to bed with you –' she gasped. ' I thought –' She hesitated. It was difficult to say what she had thought and expected. 'I thought – it would be wonderful,' she said, finally, lamely, ashamed of herself.

'You know better than that, or you wouldn't have come here,' he asserted. 'You didn't come here just for a good fuck. You said you wanted to escape from your passions.'

'Yes, I suppose so,' Lucy concurred bleakly. She hadn't imagined that escaping from her passions would mean participating in the gratification of anyone's else's.

'Dr Clock unpicks the lock,' he said. 'Look up at the ceiling.' He was standing behind his desk now, adjusting some small piece of machinery. By switching off the table lamp, he darkened the room and changed its atmosphere totally, eliminating the purple glow and leaving the orange light from the gas-fire its only illumination, before he threw another switch which made the machine, a small projector, begin to grind into motion.

'What are those things?' she asked, unable to decipher the mass of squirming, pullulating objects, blindly pushing against each other.

'Oh, they could be cells, or bacteria, or they could be maggots in the earth or in a wound – it doesn't make any difference – or they could be larger animals, even people, I'm not sure. It's films of all those things, superimposed over each other. They're all the same, it doesn't seem to make any difference what the scale of life is or even what the motive is supposed to be. It looks the same from far enough away.'

'But what does that mean, what are you trying to say?'

'You decide what you want it to mean, and it will mean just that. You can't help but be right.'

The picture covered the entire ceiling. Lucy kept looking up, held by the inexplicable activity. The colours flushed from cool to bloody, then back again, like the speeded-up view of a battlefield from high in space, or the changing of seasons. It repelled and calmed her at the same time.

'I think this is cancer cells reproducing themselves,' Dr Clock said in an explanatory, school-masterly sort of voice.

'I suppose it could be.' She was beginning to be bored and tired. 'I think I'll get dressed.'

'Yes, we've had enough for today,' he agreed, watching her search for her clothes and put them on in the light of the still continuing film, which now looked like spores exploding open, or a distant view of land under heavy bombardment.

Reaching into her handbag for mirror and comb, Lucy saw the knife. She had forgotten about it completely. She had bought it last summer while on holiday, fascinated by the ornate handle and long blade, and it had lain in her bag ever since.

It was dark outside now, and without the transfiguring purple glow, Lucy having reclaimed her pants, the room had become shabby again as when she first entered it. Dr Clock switched off the projector at last and came and stood in front of her. For the first time she was looking directly into his face, and it gave her the unnerving sensation of being transported into the future, standing in front of a mirror and studying the reflection of her own features as they would appear in about twenty years' time. They both had the same anxious, staring blue eyes with puffy sockets, the same short nose and receding chin. The only differences were those superficial ones of sex, age, and the fleshiness which dragged down his jowls and the corners of his features. Her hair would be as grey as his then, and would float about her head in the same way if she didn't tame it. As well as being frightened, she was terribly disillusioned by their resemblance. If she'd looked at him properly on entering the room, nothing at all would have happened, she was sure of that. She couldn't bear to remember how she had exposed herself to him in so many ways.

'When will you next come to see me, dear lady?' the ridiculous old creature standing before her asked in an unctous voice. 'I'm sure we can make a lot of progress, in time. Don't forget, Dr Clock cures all ills!' he tittered, and stared calculatingly, boldly, into her eyes.

Lucy was closing the last button of her macintosh. Pale, mousey blonde hair tied severely back, insignificant body encased in the stiff garment, heavy black bag on one arm, she did look rather like a prison visitor, as he had jokingly remarked when she arrived.

'Dr Clock gets a shock,' she hissed, furious with him but even more so with herself as she swooped her hand into the bag, came out with the sharp, naked knife, and pushed it into his chest where the kimono had fallen open. It sank between two ribs, up to the hilt. She'd struck as accurately as if a trained assassin. His eyes opened even further. 'It is a shock,' he gasped, sinking slowly down and forward until he lay sideways at her feet. He had abused her, but this would redress the balance of justice, Lucy thought triumphantly. She bent down and pulled the knife from his body, wiped the blade clean on his kimonoed haunch, and dropped it back into her bag. He had fallen between her and the door.

'Dr Clock, the stumbling block,' she said, stepping over him. There was no sign that she'd ever been in the room, and no one passed her in the long, dark hall, and she met no one as she let herself out of the house and walked quickly away.

HILARY BAILEY
MIDDLE CLASS MARRIAGE SAVED

PAM ZOLINE

'WHY ? SALLY. WHY ?' Ferdinand Ransome implores in a strong but anguished tone. His pain rapidly gives way to anger. As his wife stands mute he cries, 'Answer me, you bitch,' and pushes her against the gas stove.

'I DON'T understand it. I can't understand it – nothing seems to make sense any more,' groans Norman Muir, seated, with his palm against his brow, on the ottoman by the window. He turns to his wife, who stands staring over his head into the garden. One of her hands is on the mantelpiece, one is on her hip, her long hair flows down her back – it is fleet's-in night at the hodega.

'I think I'm at the beginning of a nervous breakdown,' he says, feebly, but with menace.

AND SO these two unfortunate ladies were locked up by their husbands, Sally Ransome on November 22nd and Maria Muir on December 5th. They were not kept close in fireless attics. There was no pile of straw on the floor, brawny man-servant standing guard outside the door, no faithful Poll or Meg to attend them and smuggle out messages written in blood on the torn-off edges of their chemises. Nevertheless, they were locked up.

For example, Norman Muir, now pipe-cleaner thin and not concealing his jumpiness, took three weeks off from his legal practice, and, leaving the children in the care of the au pair and a specially hired nanny, drove his wife to his aunt's house outside Lyme Regis. Ferdinand Ransome, being an architect, fortunately worked at home, He merely stopped work for a month to keep a better eye on his wife, thus missing the deadline on the designs for a new community centre on the Isle of Dogs. He mentioned this often during the month.

Picture poor Maria, in the chill hall at Lyme Regis, sadly arranging the last, pungent chrysanthemums from the cold, winter garden, while Aunt Josephine sings hits from *Oklahoma* and organises a steak and kidney pudding in the kitchen. See Sally, by the sink, putting Elastoplast on the knee of a sobbing toddler, while, with his back against the kitchen door, Ferdinand tells her that he has always loved her, always will love her so, why, why, in Christ's name, did she have to do this thing?

ALAS FOR these ladies.

Alas, too for poor Johnny Muldoon, as he lies tossing on his lonely bed in Chelsea, taking sleeping pills, listening to late-night phone-ins on the radio, rising every morning to shake the laundry's cardboard from his fresh shirt, to drink his coffee, alone, to drive off to work, to come home alone, with a kebab in a bag. There are no more quiet dinners with vulnerable, delicious faces gazing gently over the candles at him – faces as soft as fruit at its prime, at its peak of juiciness and flavour, at the instant when it is ready to fall from the branch, or be plucked, faces of women caught and dexterously held moments before the sag, sadness, withering, the decline into middle age begins. There is no more entrancement on the oriental bed, where, as the years of marriage's abrasion and familiarity peel away, his loving partners ply him with the experience of whores, the fresh delight of virgins, the greedy gratitude of old ladies when the Meals On Wheels wagon comes up with apple pudding again. Delicious scents, soft skins, and gentle words are gone. The bed is a rock, the sheets are hessian, the pillows are like logs of wood. Loneliness calls out and answers itself across the empty room. Oh, my oysters, my pearls, my blossoms, thinks Johnny. How I miss you, love you, want you. What pain are you in? What punishments are you enduring?

The silent mornings often brought a small message, scrawled hastily in the greenhouse or on the shelf of a cupboard being cleared out. The day was often broken by a quick whispered conversation on the telephone, made while one of the husbands went out for cigarettes, finished his lunch in a restaurant, dozed off in the evening.

'I found him crying in the bathroom today. He called me a whore and kicked a hole in the door. He's taken away my shoes. I want to see you. He says he loves me. He's taken away the childrens' passports. He says he'll change. He says he'll murder me. I want to see you. He's taken away my chequebook.'

FERDINAND RANSOME and Norman Muir were suddenly full of fight and stamina in this crisis. They proved unexpectedly capable of relating to their wives all day, and most of the night, if necessary.

'You're breaking my arm,' exhales Sally.

'How many times?' demands Ferdinand, pulling her raised arm a little higher up her back. They stand in the middle of a patch of brussels sprouts stumps, shielded from the house by bare fruit trees. The wind is blowing cold.

'Twice,' is Sally's groaning lie.

'It must have been more than that.'

'No. Twice. Honestly. I swear it.'

The answer does not matter. He releases her with a moan of disgust. He picks up an empty flowerpot and hurls it through the greenhouse window. '*Twice*,' he shouts. 'You bitch. *What happened?*'

'So it was every time you said you were going to the dressmaking class. That accounts for five Thursdays,' Norman Muir says remorselessly. It is half past five in the morning. His nervous energy is undiminished. 'And twice when you said you were going to see your mother. That makes seven times. So when were the other three? How does he make a living? What do they pay him? Where did he go to school? How old is he? What happened to this wife of his, then? Does he give her any money? Does he see her? *What happened?*'

How does he fuck? is what they mean. They think to get to the heart of the matter but they will only get to the prick. They will not discover how blindly and instinctively the women are running away from them and the lives they are leading for the sole purpose of accommodating the men. It is a life of the utmost boredom, intellectual and spiritual. It is a life without intimacy, since so much must be ignored in order to maintain it. Its surface is like the surface of the dining room table they polish – shiny, unyielding, and giving back, as they stand over it polishing, little reflection of themselves. It has, at its inmost core, income, status and appearances. It is a parched land, scrubland, a surreal landscape in which lie pairs and pairs of Clark's shoes, starting with tiny ones and increasing by stages in size. There are sofas, deep freezes and rolls and rolls of fitted carpet. There on the bare horizon, sits the bank manager behind his desk. There, near the Cortina, are Dr and Mrs Macintosh, friends with faces like mirrors so that they can reflect the Muirs, Ransomes, back to themselves. The husbands will never understand all this, although they have felt it on their own accounts.

AND JOHNNY MULDOON, gentle Johnny Muldoon, is walking round the park in the cold, whispering the names of the women. He cannot help them, as the wind rattles the bare branches of the trees. He cannot talk to them, as the wind strikes cold on his face. He can only wait for them, walk round the park, aching. The pain goes through him like the touch of ice on a warm palm.

ODDLY ENOUGH, for men of such different characters, the remarks made by Ferdinand Ransome and Norman Muir during their discussions with their wives had a surprising similarity. As they died, for example, they would catalogue the vices they lacked, calling on their wives to thank God that they, Ferdinand and Norman, were not your usual run of Toms, Dicks and Harrys who killed their wives in anger, lost their jobs through drink, gambled away their homes and went out for a packet of fags leaving their wives in labour on the bathroom floor and never came back for twenty years. They each concluded, on a more plangent and conciliatory note, 'I'm not a brute, am I?' There was never a reply. Truth to tell, both wives had, over the years, come slowly to think that their husbands were brutes. A distorted view, but a case could have been made out for it. Unhappily, Ferdinand and Norman, chiefly due to the corrupting position of being husbands, had, day be day, given in more and more to those momentary impulses and funny little ways we all have to the extent that, assuming their behaviour to be a normal response to certain situations, exonerating themselves as they went, they had gradually accumulated a corpus of inconsiderate behaviour which by someone given to making sweeping statements, might have been described as cruelty.

Let us be brief in our examples – we are not, after all, talking anything very rare or remarkable. Ferdinand Ransome, a man who was, on his better side, of an active, positive and sanguine temperament, was naturally inclined to be hot tempered. On a good many occasions, not liking his dinner, or a word out of turn having been spoken by wife or children during the meal, he had thrown his plate of food at the wall or swept all the dishes from the table to the floor. He once cut up Sally's new winter coat with a pair of dressmaking shears because she had bought it against his advice. He had also, during ten years of marriage, been unfaithful to his wife on the odd occasion. He confessed once, was found out once and the rest were clear rounds unless you count Sally Ransome's patches of silence and an air of uneasiness from time to time.

Norman Muir, at his best a reliable, punctilious and honest man, had, when at home, other faults. He paid attention to detail. His long, narrow finger swept the mantelpiece and the top of the fridge by sheer force of habit. He then looked neutrally at the finger. Maria kept housekeeping books which he examined monthly, doing rapid sums in his head, bringing out odd bills to prove various statistical points and mentioning the hours of work he put in to earn the family income. He also wondered what had happened to his blue socks, pondering if they might not have stayed in use if they had been repaired. He surmised that shoes might last longer if the children were persuaded not to scrape up and down walls on their way home from school, discussed the wisdom of buying fresh peas so early in the season and noticed a scratch on the surface of his mother's table. In response to Norman's eye for detail, his wife's behaviour veered between bursts of wild defiance – the papering of the sitting room in orange and scarlet is a good example – and jumpy self-defensiveness. She concealed the bill for the redecorating for an agonising eighteen months and finally sold a small ring left her be an aunt so that she could pay it. Needless to say Norman noticed the absence of the ring three weeks later during a casual spot-check of her jewellery box.

It is impossible to blame these men for their behaviour. Home, after all, is the only place where a man can kick off his shoes, slip down his braces, relax and really be himself. Nonetheless, little slips lead to greater ones, *facilis descensus Averni*, for want of a nail the kingdom was lost, for want of an early morning cup of tea the marriage was lost.

It must not be forgotten that these women, Sally and Maria, were partially enslaved by their husbands – held hostage by the children's need for parental care and upkeep, unable to face the long and dreadful road of Social Security, part time jobs and poverty with their children, unable to face leaving without them and taking the hippie trail to Katmandu. Perhaps we should not blame Norman and

Ferdinand for their behaviour; or Sally and Maria for letting them get away with it; but just put the blame fairly and squarely on the shoulders of that great Universal Grinding Company of life, the institution, marriage itself.

AND, oh dear, slowly from Johnny's flat the scents, sounds and glances of the women begin very gently to fade. The messages and little phone calls come less and less often. He knows by now that Ferdinand has not killed Sally, and that Norman has not thrown Maria, penniless and sobbing, from the house. He knows these things will not happen now. But he still waits, in case they need him, he is still lonely, he still knows that they are being punished. If they should come he would put balm on their bruises, soothe them like mares, listen to them and love them, Instead, he watches colour TV alone while the ghosts of the women circle the room in silence.

AND MEANWHILE, the women, confronted with their husbands, sound men of sterling worth, began to fail. These men had stood the test of time. They were the fathers of their children. They had paid for everything that came into the house. They were putting up a fight, they were braced, they were Actionmen. They were, moreover, paying their wives some attention at last – often disagreeable attention, but attention nonetheless. These women had lived in the corners and cupboards of their houses while the great banquet of life went on in the dining room. Only with Johnny, in secret and out of society, had the shades of Mrs Ferdinand Ransome and Mrs Norman Muir begun to deepen and thicken again. But when their husbands started to look at them again, the effect was much the same. See it like this. Sally, for example, by concerning herself with Ferdinand, by buying him his favourite pâté and getting his suit from the cleaners while he is at work, acknowledges Ferdinand's existence. By this Ferdinand knows when he comes home, that all day long and right up to the moment when she greets him, Sally has been and is admitting that Ferdinand exists. He is alive. He is important. But if he, Ferdinand, does not concentrate on Sally to the same extent, which he does not, he abolishes Sally. As in that terrifying childhood game where a group of children pretend not to see or hear another child, even walk through him on the grounds that he is intangible, Sally panics, begins to wonder if she is real, or just an empty chair with a sewing basket on one side, and a half-read library book on the floor beneath.

Now that Sally and Ferdinand are recreating each other. Johnny starts to vanish. He never had much existence anyway. He was a bunch of flowers, a dinner, a conversation, a little loving. Where is Johnny's documentation? His wife is in Strasbourg, sitting on a committee. His child is at a convent near Lyons. He has lost his birth certificate. There is even some doubt if his divorce, a Mississippi one, is legal. Watching his TV and the spiralling smoke of his Gitanes, sorrowing still for his poor ladies, with the messages and phone calls coming fainter and fewer, Johnny fades and fades.

Ferdinand and Sally, Norman and Maria, dwindle him more. He becomes a mere drop of axle grease on the grinding cogs of their marriages, almost, they begin to think, the agency for saving those great leviathans from coming to a halt, blowing up or falling to pieces in the road. Bits of conversational small change – 'Perhaps,' observes Maria, 'there wasn't all that much there in the first place.' 'He's probably,' Ferdinand remarks, 'not a bad fellow at heart' – gradually tot up to the matrimonial thirty pieces of silver in a pile on the sitting room mantelpiece.

Perhaps resolution, reconciliation, is in sight.

FERDINAND RANSOME and Norman Muir had not previously known each other but, by a coincidence, both were involved in the project to build the Isle of Dogs community centre, Norman Muir as solicitor, Ferdinand Ransome as architect. Just before Christmas, after a protracted and difficult meeting at the office of the contractor in Cavendish Street, Muir and Ransome, who had got on well during the discussions, decided to go off for a drink together. Each knew that his wife was fully accounted for, one at a matinee with her mother, the other running the cake stall at the school Christmas jumble sale, and both sensed that the crisis was at least half at an end. And both were thoroughly glad of the outing. In the crowded pub, gaily decorated for Christmas with paper chains and a tinselled Christmas tree, Muir and Ransome sat down in the only two free seats, at a table with a fair, vague-looking man, who was drinking brandy. First, Ransome bought Muir a drink, then Muir did the same for him, and in just over ten minutes both men were well into their third whiskies. The drink went to their heads rapidly, for, leading quiet lives standing guard over their womenfolk, neither Muir nor Ransome had taken a drink for weeks.

'One more. Then I must be getting home,' Muir said, getting unsteadily to his feet.

'Thanks old man. Hope you don't think I always put it away like this. To be perfectly candid I haven't been out without my wife for a couple of months. The excitement's gone to my head a bit.'

'Funny you should say that,' Muir told him. 'Position's about the same in my case.' As he went to the bar he muttered, 'You feel a bit overlooked –' and Ransome laughed. The fair man opposite smiled. He pulled the *Financial Times* from the pocket of his white raincoat, which hung over the back of the chair, and began to read.

The Ransome, taking his drink from Muir's hand, missed it. The whisky flooded over the edge of the table and on to the stranger's trousers.

'Very, very sorry,' said Ransome. 'How careless –'

'Never mind,' the other man said, scrubbing at his trousers with an immaculate handkerchief. 'No real harm done.'

'You'll have to get them cleaned,' Ransome said, groping inappropriately in his pocket. 'You must let me –'

'Nonsense,' said the other.

'What'll you have, then?'

'That's very civil of you,' said the stranger. 'I'm drinking brandy.'

Bringing back the drinks, Ransome said, 'Your wife will curse me.'

The other man slowly folded up his newspaper, put it on the table, took a drink and remarked briefly, 'No wife.' To dispel, from courtesy, any impression that he might be a homosexual – they had, after all, come to relax and drink without anxiety – he added, 'she left me.'

'That's too bad,' says Muir.

The stranger, looking at Muir with a gaze which might, or might not, contain humour, said, 'I think she was right.' The others decide that he is a simple fellow who does not care what impression he gives. Perhaps he is drunk! There is a silence. 'I wasn't very nice to her,' the stranger explains. 'I used to shout at her a lot. I wasn't faithful either. It wasn't that I couldn't keep my hands off other women. I just didn't want to.' He finished, but the silence went on. Having their full attention, he goes on, 'That wouldn't have mattered to her. I suppose. What hurt her most of all was that I didn't love her any more. So then she didn't care. Finally she had an affair with my best friend, a seedy fellow, I considered. I made a terrific fuss – hit her, harangued her incessantly and all that – and off she went. It's strange,' he said consideringly, 'how one's cuckolder always has the same character – he's a seedy, degraded fellow of infinite slyness and cunning, with a honeyed tongue and an organ like the piston of a steam engine. I beg your pardon,' he added, acknowledging the presence of the others, 'I'm afraid I was talking to myself. You don't want to hear all this.'

'Not at all, old man,' Ransome said heartily. 'I mean – well, candidly, I've been keeping an eye on mine. Wife I mean. I have the impression she's been seeing a little too much of a certain party.'

In the silence, Muir said bitterly, 'It's the same with me.'

'Oh?' said the stranger, leaning forward a little, the born extractor of confidences, widening his eyes a fraction. 'I came back from Dortmund, suddenly, myself.'

'Mine confessed,' Muir said, in the same bitter tone. 'There are times when I wish she hadn't.'

'We expect so much,' the stranger said. 'It's like not understanding mother until you're grown up. We see them so much in terms of their functions and how they treat us. 'Why are you crying little boy?' 'Mum hit me and made me cry., 'Poor little boy. Whatever for?' 'Playing with matches.' 'Well' perhaps you shouldn't –' 'Just because she said I burnt the house she didn't have to hit me like that. Boo hoo.'

The men regard him curiously. On the one hand he appears to be a normal man who has somehow survived their predicament, who has valuable information to convey. On the other hand, there is something flexible, feminine, and subtly wrong about his last remarks. The men are cautious. They will sniff him, test him, give him another chance.

'Perhaps we should introduce ourselves,' says Ransome. 'I'm Ferdinand Ransome'.

'Norman Muir.'

It is to the stranger's credit that he panics completely. He could after all, give a false name, shake the proffered hands, leave with dignity after a decent interval.

Instead, 'Oh, Christ,' shouts Johnny Muldoon, making a break for it.

'Mr Muldoon,' cries the barman, wanting payment, as Johnny flashes out through the door of the pub.

'Muldoon!' cry Ransome and Muir, after him in a trice.

Johnny ducks down a couple of turnings and slows his pace as he realises he has lost the husbands. But, suddenly, there is the roar of an engine. Glancing round he sees the green Cortina, Ransome at the wheel, Muir in the passenger seat, leaning forward eagerly, coming up the road at speed. He just has time to flatten himself against the wall as the car mounts the pavement, brushes him and races off down the road again. Ransome has his thumb on the horn. Muir has turned round in his seat. He is mouthing and making a v-sign.

Johnny breathes out, a long gasp. He feels the ache in his shoulder where it hit the wall. Looking down, he sees that the car has torn his trousers.

He finds himself in Oxford Street, very tired, pushed and shoved by women with shopping bags, people rushing home from work. His shoulder still aches. His legs feel like jelly. Isolated (wife in Strasbourg, daughter near Lyons, best friend in New York) breathing slow, tired, slack, limp, he can hardly put one foot in front of the other. The hurrying people, the Christmas lights, the booming 'Silent Night' coming from a store – he wonders if he is here at all. Have they really killed him, these men? Have they, Actionman (German Stormtrooper, British commando, American Marine) killed him, Victimman, (Jewish violinist, Austrian farmer, Vietnamese peasant)? Are they trained killers – little boys mustn't cry – these fighters for King and Country – be a brave soldier now – these defenders of hearth and home? Will they always slay the dragon and kill the maiden and blow up her castle by accident, as well? Will they always clank about, showing off in their armour, treading on the crawling baby with an ironshot foot, carelessly waving their swords and slashing open a beauteous maiden's cheek?

And so Johnny, defenceless as a shelled lobster, drags himself home to bed. The room is quiet now, quiet as the grave. The women's ghosts have been laid.

But it is all very well to leave our Johnny thus – betrayed, caught, nailed to the cross by the iron, authoritarian hand of marriage. To leave out women thus – ashy and ghastly, mincing themselves through their own mincers, going round and round washing out their own obstinate stains in their own automatic machines, darning up the rents Johnny left in them with grey wool to match the fabric. To leave our husbands thus, again in Technicolor and 3-D, leaping out of bed in the morning dressed as Superman.

Being reasonable people we know that Johnny is only dead in terms of a metaphor, and it generally takes more than a comparison to kill a man. There may be more to our tale. We may not have mentioned that Johnny, as well, as being a cuckolder was an architect. Imagine Ferdinand Ransome's face over breakfast when he reads the letter explaining tactfully that after the unresolved difficulties of the meeting, the board had decided that the might like to work jointly with another architect, with much experience in the field. The name he was given was, of course, that of the Muldoon. Ransome, deeply wounded in two ways, naturally invited the board to choose between himself and Muldoon. The board naturally preferred Muldoon. Or did we say that part of Norman Muir's distress about his wife was spin-off from a sensation of insecurity about the concerns of his firm ? Alas for Norman, although a dab hand at checking the stamp money, he had failed to comprehend the profound dishonesty of his partner, who, it turned out, had embezzled from the clients of the firm something like £50,000. All this was tough on Sally and Maria, who, having sacrificed much for their marriages, suddenly discovered the security of their homes to be threatened, at a time of galloping inflation, and their husbands, faced with many problems, less than sympathetic and attentive. Did we hint at the existence of the beautiful Beatrice Hereford the clever, rich, divorced mother of the delightful five-year-old Simonetta, who had been in love with Johnny for two years ?

Well, all these things are true. It cannot be a wholly wicked world, where on the one hand the laws of cause and effect operate so consistently, and, on the other hand, blind chance throws rags and riches, crowns and crosses at us with so profligate a hand.

CLAUD COCKBURN: DIAL E FOR EZRA

IN 1927 I was living in Berlin. Berlin was then a cheap and pulsatingly open-hearted city in which you could buy more food and drink, and more excitement and cultural stimulus, than in any other city of central or Western Europe. I had sold a story to *The Dial* (the dollars from *The Dial* amounted to about a quarter's installment of the annual payment for the Oxford Travelling Fellowship on which I was living while insinuating myself as an uninvited and unpaid apprentice into the Berlin offices of the London *Times*); and this brought much euphoria to myself and many friends. A few weeks after the publication of the story and the arrival of the cheque there came another sort of communication. This was a letter written in blue ink or possibly some unusual type of chalk on a sheet of thin brown paper apparently torn from a lavatory roll. The message was brief. It read 'Dial story fine Hurrah. Any chance see you this city merry month May. Pound.'

My euphoria increased. It would be fatuous to suggest that at that time I would rather have had praise from Ezra Pound than the dollar cheque, but to have them both was intoxicating. I saw with dismay that the letter posted in Vienna had been addressed to me care of the New York office of *The Dial* and forwarded from there, and it was almost the end of May. I hurried from the office and took the night train to Vienna. Arrived there, I discovered that in my excitement of the prospect of actually meeting the poet I had somewhere dropped and lost his letter and was therefore without his address. I did not know Vienna very well at that time, nor had I much idea of the likely habits of an eminent American poet roaming central Europe. Naturally I knew from photographs what Pound looked like and for a while I thought the best thing to do would be to pace up and down the Kaertmer Strasse in the hope of seeing his red beard suddenly flame out among the window shoppers. Then, the heat being intense, and my feet growing weary, it would be just as sensible to go and sit, if neccessary for hours, in the Café Zentral. It was of this café that the essayist Polgar had written: – 'The Café Zentral is not a coffee-house like other coffee-houses but rather a way of looking at life; a way, that is, of which the inner-most content consists in not looking at life.'

But the Café Zentral corresponded to the Romanisches Café in Berlin. And I reasoned that if in Berlin I were looking, however hopelessly, for an eminent American writer my best bet would be to sit about in the Romanisches Café. It also seemed to me that life could not possibly be so arranged that I should have come all this way from Berlin to Vienna to meet Ezra Pound and then fail to meet him. I was therefore not much surprised when on entering the café I immediately saw that red beard jutting and wagging above a table in front of a banquette against the wall on the further side of the room.

I introduced myself. With a loud ha-ha, Pound shouted the title of my *Dial* story and for the next few minutes as he talked I experienced that vigorous massaging of the spirit which has caused so many writers who then were young to remember that whatever his subsequent wickedness of thought and action – and it was indeed great – Pound was a man of actively generous heart, eager to pour out his time and energy encouraging people who might quite likely be wasting both, and to puff away with the bellows of his own genius at any spark which he conceived might thus be assisted to burst into flame.

What was he doing in Vienna? 'I have decided,' he said, grinning over the tip of his beard, 'to shift the cultural centre of Europe from Paris to Vienna. I am here to start a magazine.'

Throughout this preliminary conversation a greyish personage who had been sitting with Pound before my arrival had been listening intently. He to my mind had the appearance of an international spy. One's instincts in these matters are usually correct and some hours later I discovered that being an international spy was in fact his business. But it was not a business which Pound was aware of. The conversation which followed was a typical example of the kind of imbroglio in which Pound first harmlessly and then disastrously involved himself. The greyish man, whom we will describe as Herr Spy, had somehow convinced Pound that he, Herr Spy, could mobilise both financial and cultural resources in Vienna which would ensure the immediate launching of a powerful literary magazine such as would in fact transfer the cultural centre of Europe to Vienna. The man had no capacity to deliver such goods. He was in fact playing Pound for a sucker. And this, by hindsight, had some significance.

Consider the period. We are approaching the end of the 1920s. Pound at that time considered himself with some justification to be among the few literati who closely observed the innards of the capitalist system. And in some areas he really did have what the Germans call finger-tip-feeling for the workings of the system and for what actually goes on. His famous Canto on the subject of Sir Basil Zaharoff, the prototype of all great international armament manufacturers, proves that he did have that feeling and could express it with devastating poetic imagination. But precisely in the schizophrenia and alienations of the capitalist world, the poet is necessarily both observer and outsider. In other words, he is always to some extent the sucker. He knows something but does not know enough. Before he became a Marxist, the author of *La Trahison des Clercs* wrote of the disillusionment of the idealistic writer who after supporting some cause always was apt to experience the sense of being 'Une fois de plus dupe de quelque chose'. Neither then in Vienna, nor all those years later in disastrous Rome, was Pound aware of being the dupe of anything at all. Yet he was.

So there they sat side by side on the banquette, the poet and Herr Spy. Each believed to be successfully exploiting the other. Herr Spy was an international Spy in the strictest sense of the word. He worked for an international spy bureau in Brussels which sold secret or stolen information, and very often purely invented information, to any government or other agency which would pay for it. He had, I suppose, rather less knowledge of the basic forces at work in the world that did Pound. But he had that quick mental sensitivity of the professional crook which enabled him to judge nicely the kind of chat which would appeal to Pound. He had successfully convinced Pound that he, Herr Spy, understood the working of financial and cultural Vienna and could deliver whatever goods might seem desirable to the American tourist wandering through the cultural bazaars of central Europe. Pound for his part was, although I suppose he would have denied it, an almost childlike incarnation of what used to be called the American Dream.

Only a few years earlier Ford Madox Ford had started in Paris a magazine which he proclaimed was to 'Raise the dun-coloured banner of all Middle-Westishness of the world'. Pound's conception of middle-westishness was certainly different from Ford's. But he did, whether he would have admitted it or not, have a belief that somehow the United States, or rather the spirit of America, could play a major role in liberating the soul of the world. And in his attitudes towards banking and usury, he expressed in fact the simple philosophy of the old middle westerner in constant fear of being exploited by the city slicker. His ludicrous and ulti-mately disgusting anti-semitism, stemming from an identi-fication of Jews with high finance, was a typical example of middle westishness of an old-fashioned kind standing defensively against city slickerdom. And since like so many of his generation in the United States, he lacked even the elements of a Marxist grasp of economic realities, he was vulnerable to almost every wind of Leftish doctrine which brewed. Simultaneously, if paradoxically, these Leftish winds were ususlly a re-puff of much older American winds. Even now in the Café Zentral I was aware that in his heart Pound was constantly humming the Battle Hymn of the Republic. He was trampling out the vintage where the grapes of cultural wrath were stored, and was preparing at any minute to loose the fateful lightning of a terrible swift sword. As Christ died to make men holy he would die to make men free in spirit, and Herr Spy was the man to help him to do it.

Having lived for many years in central Europe. I took it for granted that Pound would understand me when I spoke of the looming menace of facism. By what hind-sightedly can be seen as an ironic shrug, Pound spoke of Mussolini as a mere clown, and when I suggested that he and his movement might be symptomatic of something far more serious he felt that the conversation was becoming frivolous, that I was trying to introduce entirely superficial political considerations into a serious discussion of the basic cultural situation. Yet at the same time I already felt so strongly about the impending menace that I did not refrain from reminding him of the old German nursery jingle about the

bed bug which sits on the wall, which can dance, so finely
and which again sits on the wall, lurking.

> '*Scham einmal die Wanze an*
> *Wie die Wanze tanzen kann:*
> *Auf der Mauer, auf Lauer*
> *Sitzt die grosse Wanze.*'

Herr Spy listened with the keenest attention, keeping his
face entirely noncommital. He had no more idea than Pound,
probably rather less, of what precisely I was talking about,
but had just cottoned on to the idea that I was in some way
connected with the London *Times* and that therefore anything that I said might be a reflection of the views of the
big men in Printing House Square, indeed of the British
government, and therefore worthy of immediate sale to
some idiotic bureau in some capital or other. As a result of
this typical misconception, Herr Spy had by now become
more interested in me than in Ezra Pound. So that when
Pound had to leave to keep an appointment with George
Antheil, the composer, Herr Spy without wasting much
time on preliminary discussion, propounded to me a scheme
by which we would both burglarise and bribe our way into
the Austrian Foreign Office. Having secured the secrets of
that office, we would join in selling them on the best markets.
He took it for granted that a man holding some sort of card
as a representative of the London *Times* would be of enormous use in this enterprise. He was momentarily chilled
by my question as to whether we should know anything
more after bribing and burglarising our way into that
office than we already knew. He gave me a look, which I
have always been accustomed to, showing that the man who
is talking to one cannot make up his mind whether one is
inconceivably naïve and innocent, or almost desperately
cunning. It is one of the rewards of the essentially naïve to
observe the unease in the eyes of the essentially corrupt.

I saw Pound several times before returning to Berlin, but
there was an interval of nearly a year before I saw him again,
this time in Paris. I was still living on the last instalments
of my Oxford Fellowship and still hanging about the office
of the London *Times*. I was naturally writing a novel but I
had not written any short stories since that one in *The Dial*.

I was therefore in some penury in a half-roofed studio about a couple of miles on the south side of Paris, on the hillside at Fontenay-aux-Roses, which was inhabited by the only ghost which I have ever seen. This was the ghost of a White Russian émigré general who had died on the three packing cases which, dragged together, had formed his bed and now formed mine. I used to wonder whether the snow which in the late winter sometimes drifted through the holes in the roof made him feel at home. At other times enormous rainbows used to form themselves over Paris and one could see one end planted planted somewhere near the tomb of Napoleon and the other beyond Vincennes, which at that time was in the process of electing its first Communist mayor.

Paris at that time was not at all a cheap or openhearted town. The boom of the late 1920's was in progress. In practice this meant that the rich got richer and the poor got poorer. And even the rich French were torn with anxiety lest either war or revolution break out before they could satisfactorily finish living luxuriously and dying in their beds. The only truly cheerful people about were the American expatriates. Some of them had inherited and many of them had earned enough dollars to enable them to buy enough depreciated francs to live happily in a city which to them still represented all that was best and finest.

I could not afford, nor did I wish to afford, tram fare from Fontenay-aux-Roses further than the Boulevard Montparnasse. For there were then three cafés on that Boulevard where one was certain to meet the international intelligentsia as one previously had been at the Romanisches Café in Berlin or the Café Zentral in Vienna. It was, I think, at the Café de la Rotonde that I ran into Ezra Pound. In the course of a conversation I happened to mention to him that there had just arrived in Paris an uncle of mine who was at the time a prominent banker in Montreal. Pound, with his passionate interest in usury, was eager to have converse with a banker on intimate terms. Could I arrange a meeting between himself and my uncle? I replied that nothing could be easier since my uncle, for his part, was passionately interested in literature and would have been happy to rush out of a meeting of bank directors at any moment on the chance of meeting a poet.

The dinner which I arranged for my uncle and Ezra

Pound could not be considered a success, except possibly from my own point of view as a spectator of the encounter. Pound had no interest in discussing poetry with my uncle but wished to get right down to a thorough discussion of the mechanics of the banking business. My uncle, to whom the mechanics of the banking business were in the main tedious, kept brushing aside Pound's enquiries and sought in his turn to extract from Pound some explanations and illuminations of the craft of poesy. However, both joined in proffering advice regarding my own best course for the future.

My uncle was determined that I should become the London *Times* correspondent in New York. This was a course which I myself approved because I believed then that by observing Wall Street at close quarters I should be able to ascertain whether the Marxists were right in their analysis of the situation or whether the anti-Marxists were right in stating that the United States and particularly 'Der Fordismus' had solved the problems of capitalism, and made a monkey out of Marx. Both the banker and the poet were realistic. They spent a good deal of time explaining to me the desirability of securing a really first-class bootlegger in New York and avoiding at all costs the risk of blinding oneself by drinking the wrong kind of liquor.

Pound too was favourable to the notion of my becoming the New York correspondent of the London *Times*. I have a feeling that he already envisaged a possibility in which the New York office of that newspaper would somehow become a cultural centre such as had for unaccountable reasons failed to blossom in Vienna.

In order that the evening should not prove a total flop, I begged Pound at least to recite a few lines from one of his Cantos. This he did, and brought tears of appreciation into the eyes of my uncle. It seemed a pity that there was no way in which my uncle could reciprocate by, for example, reciting a few items from the Bank of Montreal. I left them talking, still totally at cross purposes, in order to catch the last tram back to my studio and the ghost of the Czarist General.

MONUMENT BY MICHAEL ROTHENSTEIN

MILES: MEETING ALLEN GINSBERG

In the Spring of 1970 I finally moved from London to the United States. The American poet Allen Ginsberg had offered me a job archiving his enormous collection of tape recordings. Though the tapes were lodged in the Allen Ginsberg Collection at Columbia University, they had no tape editing facilities and, since Ginsberg was living on his farm in upstate New York, I thought it better to take them all up there.

The work lasted through that summer. The editing took all winter and was done in New York City. The final electronic mastering I did in Fantasy Studios in Berkeley, California. The job was completed in June 1971

Another time, two years later, I was living in New York City and began making 'delayed' journal notes. These fragments are about the first summer on Ginsberg's farm.

WHEN Sue and I first arrived on Allen Ginsberg's farm, Peter was on speed. It made him terribly paranoid. He thought that the red-necks were going to come up from town and kill us all. He thought his portable Sony TV was watching him and attacked it with an iron bar. He did in its batteries too for good measure. Denese was annoyed about the TV so he had to get another one but in three days he smashed that up as well.

He thought a lot about Allen's views on sex and decided that the inmates of the house might fuck the horse. Accordingly he went to sleep in the barn to protect it.

His withdrawal was anguished and very painful to witness. His voice was like gravel – his 'peter's voice' he called it. He'd lived several years in India. He had boisterous speedy humour when he was up, which counterbalanced the torment as he tried to kick. We all sat around the dinner table eating while outside Peter lay on the stone path, banging his head on a rock, crying and moaning, cursing himself. 'Why do I do it? It's poison, it's fucking poison!'

Allen hovered round, wringing his hands, helpless, offering advice, offering that they chant together the Hindu prayers they learned in India to ease the pain. Peter angrily retorting: 'That stuff doesn't work! You don't really believe in all that chanting do you?'

Allen, sorrowful, sat with him, worrying, wiping away the sweat as Peter burned up and writhed on the damp evening grass. Eventually Allen came in to eat.

'Go and get your camera. Film Peter,' he said.

'No I couldn't,' said Gordon, 'Peter's a friend.'

'He'll thank you for it later, if he gets over it. And maybe it'll show someone else what speed'll do to you! You *should* film it. It's real. It's much more real than all those sunsets and trees you film . . .' Allen was quite insistent.

Gordon slowly shook his head and crouched low over the table, not looking up.

Allen was almost shouting, 'That's what being a film-maker is about. Showing things as they are. Well that's Peter out there groaning. That's how he is!'

Allen was suffering almost as much as Peter.

'Yeah, go-wan. Why not?' demanded Denese. She'd done everything possible. Their biggest worry was that Peter had still more hidden round the farm, and that he'd have to go through his withdrawal over again.

He had sold letters from Kerouac, Neal Cassidy and Allen and spent $12,000 on speed in a matter of months. He had it hidden all over the place and if he went down to Manhattan he had friends who would give him more. Allen was determined that he kick it. That was why he bought the farm.

Peter's voice eventually returned to normal. He stopped ordering his brother about so much. He became less distant and more warm and friendly. It had been a terrible period. His brother Julius had taken the brunt of it. He is a catatonic and simply did what Peter said without speaking or dissenting. Peter made him carry heavy rocks all day or dig the soybean patch in the hot summer sun.

Peter began to work compulsively. Soybeans were good for you. He would plant some. Maybe an acre. He fenced off land with posts and wire and planted frantically. He built a larger fence for the chickens though we were never able to hatch out any eggs because Julius would always disturb the hens in the mornings before we got up. Peter began to fence the land, all 70-odd acres of it. Each day he would disappear with Julius and would return for the evening meal, still filled with energy, his body burned brown in the sun. Allen was relieved. The farm had worked. It had broken

Peter's addiction. Every dollar spent was worth it.

Nathaniel Tarn came and spent a night the same time that Carl Solomon visited. Allen wrote 'Howl' for Carl Solomon. Carl called his mother as soon as he arrived from Crain's drugstore which was where the Greyhound dropped its once daily load from the big city 250 miles away.

Allen talked long to Carl's mother, assuring her that her son would be OK. That evening Carl and Allen lounged in the living-room, Carl reclining on the settee and looking like the famous photograph of Apollinaire.

'We're not young and pretty any more,' said Allen.

'No, but we can be old and bestial,' replied Carl and they looked at each other and laughed.

The conversation took a political turn at one point and Carl quickly said that he couldn't discuss things like that because his uncle wouldn't approve of it and it made him nervous. This was the same uncle who Carl worked for in 1953 and who Carl persuaded to publish William Burroughs's *Junkie* and Jack Kerouac's *Trissessa* and *Maggie Cassidy*, in funny pulp paperback editions with lurid covers.

Carl and Nathaniel talked at length about French poetry.

In the morning Nathaniel came down to breakfast dressed in what would have been the appropriate clothes if he was staying the weekend at an English country house – white trousers and tennis shoes. He stood at the foot of the stair and looked in vain for a place to wash. His face took on an air of disbelief as he looked out of the window. There in the garden stood Peter, legs astride, bent over washing his ass with great care.

'I see,' said Nathaniel. Then realised everyone was smiling at him and saw the joke.

SITTING in the dusty attic of Allen's farm. Flies buzzing at the window, the space between screen and glass deep piled with their dusty little corpses. Thick mist obscuring the lake, someone playing boogie ragtime on the piano below and Allen coughing with a chill in his woodpanelled room as he reads Agnew's McCarthyite speech on network media news distortion. It's hard to believe in this new electric consciousness, this feels like old human consciousness all along but this time round it's chrome plated. Dusty copies of *Playboy* and *New Yorker* in boxes on the floor.

A large lion with stuffed head snarling spreadeagled on the dusty floor. Bagged in Africa by Gregory Corso's ex-girlfriend's father it has finished up here looking through cold mist to the rust-red brown and white barn (traditional colours) where Bessie the cow lives. When it's quiet the seventy times an hour click in the pipes can be heard as the gravity pressure pump shoots water by the cupful up the hill to the buried tank above the house, using no gas, electricity or windmill. The ultimate ecological system. Poor dusty old lion, his snout in a perpetual snarl, yellowing fangs shat upon and spotted by New York State flies.

Yesterday Bessie the cow came into the kitchen and had some cake, fed to her by ecstatic Peter who kissed her and slapped her all over. Even Julius smiled. Bessie ate some red apples before leaving. Her shy calf wouldn't come in, looking in frightened through the open door with sad brown eyes, a little tear on her cheek. The sadness of cows. Allen says he couldn't have children, how could he perpetuate the pain? He is looking forward to the escape of death. That life for him is not the search for happiness but the avoidance of pain, to keep the wolf from the door and avoid physical pain. That life is very much shorter than anyone thinks. He recently returned from Jack Kerouac's funeral. Cassidy also dead of course.

A Tibetan tanka brought from India by Allen in 1963. Avolekteshvera hanging in his frame of Chinese silk by the window silently absorbing Allen's slow composition of Blake tunes on broken piano or tootling pump-organ, windy notes whistling forth to accompany Allen's deep bass voice. Pale sunlight in rundown nice old room. Broken down settee with dirty cover. Julius's boots neatly side by side. Peter shouting outside. Through the window Gordon passes carrying pails to the barn. A secure refuge from machine metal city. But for Allen there's no escape because he can feel the pain. Furried brow. He hurries to the telephone to sit on little child's chair by the door and receive horror news from New York, LA, San Francisco and to call *NY Times* to angrily complain about yet another warped piece of reporting.